The Library of Paul Francis Webster

Auction
Wednesday, April 24, 1985 at 2 p.m.

Exhibition
Thursday, April 18,   9:30 a.m. to 5 p.m.
Friday, April 19,   9:30 a.m. to 5 p.m.
Saturday, April 20,   9:30 a.m. to 5 p.m.
Sunday, April 21,   1 p.m. to 5 p.m.
Monday, April 22,   9:30 a.m. to 5 p.m.
Tuesday, April 23,   9:30 a.m. to 5 p.m.

In sending absentee bids this catalogue
may be referred to as 5313 "WEBSTER"

Cover illustration: Lot 73

SOTHEBY'S

FOUNDED 1744

1334 York Avenue (at 72nd Street)
New York, NY 10021
Cable: Parkgal, New York
Telex: New York 232643 (SPB UR)
Telephone: (212) 606-7000

Catalogues $25 at the gallery,
$30 by mail, $35 overseas

List of post sale price results
will be sent to all catalogue purchasers

Experts in Charge
Jane O'Connor, 606-7385
Fanny Mallary, 606-7385
Mary-Jo Kline, 606-7385
Jay Dillon, 606-7385
Selby Kiffer, 606-7385

Absentee Bids
Roberta Louckx, 606-7414

Shipping
Eileen Baral, 606-7511

Purchaser Payments
Diane Lahey, 606-7492

Consignor Payments
Richard Morreale, 606-7310

24 Hour Sale Information
Recorded announcements of
current auctions and exhibitions
212-606-7245

Expert Departments

American Decorative Arts & Furniture
Leslie B. Keno, 606-7130
William W. Stahl
David Dufour

American Folk Art
Nancy Druckman, 606-7225

American Indian, African & Oceanic Art
Ellen Napiura, 606-7325

American Paintings, Drawings & Sculpture
Peter B. Rathbone, 606-7280
Martha Richardson
Eda Martin

Antiquities
Richard M. Keresey, 606-7328
Fatma Turkkan-Wille

Arms & Armour
J. David Wille, 606-7250
Dan C. Schlenoff

Art Nouveau & Art Deco
Barbara E. Deisroth, 606-7170
Sarah Hill

Books and Manuscripts
David N. Redden, 606-7385
Mary-Jo Kline (Americana)
Fanny Mallary
Jane M. O'Connor
George S. Snyder (Judaica & Maps)
Jay Dillon
Thomas P. Clarke, Consultant

Chinese Art
Timothy S. Sammons, 606-7332
James J. Lally
Arnold Chang (Paintings), 606-7334
Carol Conover
Mee Seen Loong
Theow-Huang Tow

Coins
Robert S. Archer, 606-7391

Collectibles
Dana Hawkes, 606-7424

Contemporary Paintings, Drawings & Sculpture
Lucy Havelock-Allan, 606-7254
Leslie Prouty

English Furniture
George Read, 606-7220
Robert C. Woolley

European Furniture
Thierry Millerand, 606-7220
Phillips Hathaway

European Works of Art & Tapestries
J. David Wille, 606-7250

Impressionist & Modern Paintings, Drawings & Sculpture
David J. Nash, 606-7360
Shary E. Grossman
John L. Tancock
Barbara Pallenberg (West Coast), (213) 274-0340
Kevin Buchanan
Meredith Britz
Linda Kramer (Drawings), 606-7154

Islamic Works of Art
Richard M. Keresey, 606-7328

Japanese Art
Jane Oliver, 606-7338
Annette Kluss

Jewelry
John D. Block, 606-7392
Paul Russo
Jacqueline Fay (Antique)
Lisa Hubbard (West Coast), (415) 986-4982
Tracy Sherman
Alexander Guest
Nan Summerfield (Arcade)

Judaica
Jay Weinstein, 606-7387
Deborah Epstein

Latin American Paintings
Sharon Schultz, 606-7290
Anthony Grant

Musical Instruments
Charles Rudig, 606-7190

19th Century European Paintings & Drawings
Nancy Harrison, 606-7140
Howard Rutkowski
Benjamin F. Doller

19th Century Furniture, Decorations & Works of Art
Elaine Whitmire, 606-7285

Old Master Paintings & Drawings
George Wachter, 606-7230
Heidi Chin
Arabella Bailey (Drawings)

Paperweights & Glass
Debe Cuevas, 606-7170

Photographs
Beth Gates-Warren, 606-7240
Anne Horton (West Coast), (415) 986-4982

Porcelain: European & Chinese Export
Letitia Roberts, 606-7180
Debe Cuevas

Portrait Miniatures and Chess Sets
Sarah D. Coffin, 606-7420

Pre-Columbian Art
Fatma Turkkan-Wille, 606-7330
Richard M. Keresey

Prints
Marc E. Rosen, 606-7117
Susan Pinsky
Ruth Ziegler
Tara Reddi
Mary Bartow

Rugs and Carpets
William Ruprecht, 606-7380
Grace Yeomans

Russian Art, Icons, Objets de Vertu
Gerard Hill, 606-7150

Silver, Watches
Kevin L. Tierney, 606-7160
Ian Irving
Daryn Schnipper (Watches)

Sotheby's Arcade Auctions
Michael B. Grogan, 606-7410
Jean H. Witmer, 606-7410
Wiebke Moore (Decorations), 606-7409
Jennifer Roth (Fine Arts), 606-7516
Nan Summerfield (Jewelry), 606-7392
David Gallager (Furniture), 606-7408
Mary Jo Otsea (Rugs), 606-7380

Client Service Departments

Appraisals
Michael Grogan, 606-7440

Bids
Roberta Louckx, 606-7414

Catalogue Subscriptions
To order catalogues & price lists:
(617) 229-2282
For inquiries or difficulties:
Katheryn Jeffery, 606-7430

Client Advisory Services
Elizabeth F. Robbins, 606-7302
Eunice S. Carroll, 606-7427
Jane Wyeth, 606-7469
Nancy Forster, 606-7304

Complaints
Linda Burns, 606-7467

Consignor Payments
Paul Cervino, 606-7310
Gail Skelly

Corporate Collections
Pamela Brown Sherer, 606-7442

Trusts and Estates
Warren P. Weitman, Jr., 606-7198

Exhibitions
Alfred Bristol, 606-7460

International Office
Elena Echarte Lord, 606-7400

Legal
Marjorie E. Stone, 606-7175

Museum Services
Grace Lowe, 606-7456
William Woolfenden (Consultant)

Personnel
Pat Baxter, 606-7202

Press Office
David Yudain, 606-7176
Batya Knapp Monder

Purchaser Billing & Payment
Lola Capel, 606-7484
Constance Adamec (Arcade), 606-7147

Real Estate
Lynn Rutherford, 606-7690

Restoration (Furniture)
John Stair, 860-5446

Shipping & Customs Inquiries
Eileen Baral, 606-7511

Special Events
Hilary Cushing, 606-7375

Sales Conducted by

John L. Marion, James J. Lally, John D. Block, David J. Nash, Robert C. Woolley, William W. Stahl, Jr., Julian Barran, Eunice S. Carroll, Michael B. Grogan, Gerard J. Hill, Lisa Hubbard, Annette Kluss, Nicholas Rayner, David N. Redden, Marc E. Rosen, William F. Ruprecht, Pamela Brown Sherer, Jean H. Witmer, Richard S. Wolf
Department of Consumer Affairs Auctioneers Licensed Numbers (respectively): 524728, 718514, 733768, 764786, 678346, 760961, 795766, 738576, 767877, 761969, 794848, 793375, 792131, 736142, 690713, 794917, 767154, 778346, 793869.

If you cannot reach a specific department or have any difficulties, please call our client service representative, Linda Burns, at 606-7467.

Conditions of Sale

This catalogue, as amended by any posted notices or oral announcements during the sale, is Sotheby Parke Bernet Inc's and the Consignor's entire agreement with the purchaser relative to the property listed herein. The following Conditions of Sale, the Terms of Guarantee and any glossary contained herein are the complete and only terms and conditions on which all property is offered for sale. The property will be offered by us as agent for the Consignor, unless the catalogue indicates otherwise.

1. The authenticity of the Authorship of property listed in the catalogue is guaranteed as stated in the Terms of Guarantee; except as provided therein all property is sold "**AS IS**," and neither we nor the Consignor make any warranties or representations of the correctness of the catalogue or other description of the physical condition, size, quality, rarity, importance, provenance, exhibitions, literature or historical relevance of the property and no statement anywhere, whether oral or written, shall be deemed such a warranty or representation. Prospective bidders should inspect the property before bidding to determine its condition, size and whether or not it has been repaired or restored. We and the Consignor make no representations and warranties as to whether the purchaser acquires any copyrights, including but not limited to any reproduction rights, in the property.

2. A premium of 10% of the successful bid price will be added thereto and is payable by the purchaser as part of the total purchase price.

3. We reserve the right to withdraw any property before sale.

4. Unless otherwise announced by the auctioneer, all bids are per lot as numbered in the catalogue.

5. We reserve the right to reject any bid. The highest bidder acknowledged by the auctioneer will be the purchaser. In the event of any dispute between bidders, or in the event of doubt on our part as to the validity of any bid, the auctioneer will have the final discretion either to determine the successful bidder or to reoffer and resell the article in dispute. If any dispute arises after the sale, our sale record is conclusive. Although in our discretion we will execute order bids or accept telephone bids as a convenience to clients who are not present at auctions, we are not responsible for any errors or omissions in connection therewith.

6. If the auctioneer decides that any opening bid is below the value of the article offered, he may reject the same and withdraw the article from sale, and if, having acknowledged an opening bid, he decides that any advance thereafter is insufficient, he may reject the advance.

7. On the fall of the auctioneer's hammer, title to the offered lot will pass to the highest bidder acknowledged by the auctioneer, subject to fulfillment by such bidder of all the conditions set forth herein, and such bidder thereupon (a) assumes full risk and responsibility therefor, (b) will sign a confirmation of purchase thereof, and (c) will pay the full purchase price therefor or such part as we may require. In addition to other remedies available to us by law, we reserve the right to impose a late charge of 1½% per month of the total purchase price if payment is not made in accordance with the conditions set forth herein. The late charge will be imposed pro rata for periods of less than one month. All property must be removed from our premises by the purchaser at his expense not later than 3 business days following its sale and,

if it is not so removed, (i) a handling charge of 1% of the purchase price per month until its removal will be payable to us by the purchaser, with a minimum of 5% for any property not so removed within 60 days after the sale, and (ii) we may send the purchased property to a public warehouse for the account, risk and expense of the purchaser. If any applicable conditions herein are not complied with by the purchaser, in addition to other remedies available to us and the Consignor by law, including without limitation the right to hold the purchaser liable for the total purchase price, we at our option may either (a) cancel the sale, retaining as liquidated damages all payments made by the purchaser or (b) resell the property at public auction without reserve, and the purchaser will be liable for any deficiency, costs, including handling charges, the expenses of both sales, our commission on both sales at our regular rates, all other charges due hereunder and incidental damages. In addition, a defaulting purchaser will be deemed to have granted us a security interest in, and we may retain as collateral security for such purchaser's obligations to us, any property in our possession owned by such purchaser regardless of when we may acquire possession. We shall have all of the rights afforded a secured party under the New York Uniform Commercial Code with respect to such property and we may apply against such obligations all monies held or received by us for the account of, or due from us to, such purchaser. At our option, payment will not be deemed to have been made in full until we have collected funds represented by checks, or, in the case of bank or cashier's checks, we have confirmed their authenticity.

8. Lots marked with □ immediately preceding the lot number are offered subject to a reserve, which is the confidential minimum price below which such lot will not be sold. We may implement such reserves by bidding on behalf of the Consignor. In certain instances, the Consignor may pay less than the standard commission rate where a lot is "bought-in" to protect its reserve. Where the Consignor is indebted to or has a monetary guarantee from us, and in certain other instances, where we or our affiliated companies may have an interest in the offered lots and the proceeds therefrom other than our commissions, we may bid therefor to protect such interests.

9. Unless exempted by law, the purchaser will be required to pay the combined New York State and local sales tax or any applicable compensating use tax of another state on the total purchase price. The rate of such combined tax is 8¼% in New York City and ranges from 4¼% to 8¼% elsewhere in New York State.

10. These Conditions of Sale as well as the purchaser's and our respective rights and obligations hereunder shall be governed by and construed and enforced in accordance with the laws of the State of New York. By bidding at an auction, whether present in person or by agent, order bid, telephone or other means, the purchaser shall be deemed to have consented to the jurisdiction of the state courts of, and the federal courts sitting in, the State of New York.

11. We are not responsible for the acts or omissions of carriers or packers of purchased lots, whether or not recommended by us. Packing and handling of purchased lots by us is at the entire risk of the purchaser.

12. In no event will our liability to a purchaser exceed the purchase price actually paid.

Terms of Guarantee for Books, Manuscripts and Memorabilia

We guarantee the authenticity and condition of each book and manuscript and memorabilia of historical interest catalogued herein on the terms and conditions set forth below:

1. Physical Condition. Except for books in original parts, serial publications and any lot containing more than one item, or unless otherwise indicated in the respective catalogue description, we guarantee that each book and manuscript is complete in both text and illustrations and generally is in such physical condition as may reasonably be expected considering the age and provenance. If within two weeks from the date we deliver a purchased book or manuscript, the original purchaser of record tenders to us such purchased book or manuscript in the same condition as when sold and it is established that the catalogue description of the physical condition of such lot (as amended by any posted notices or oral announcements during the sale) is not substantially correct based upon a fair reading of the catalogue as a whole including the terms of any Glossary contained herein, the sale of such lot shall be rescinded and the original purchase price refunded.

2. Authenticity. Unless otherwise indicated in the respective catalogue description or unless physical inspection would reveal self-evident lack of authenticity, we guarantee the authenticity of the signature of autographed material, the accuracy of the edition number designation of books and the provenance of memorabilia of historical interest, the value of which derives solely from its historical significance. If within five years from the date of sale of a purchased lot, the original purchaser of record tenders to us a purchased lot in the same condition as when sold and it is established that the catalogue

description of the lot as it relates to its authenticity (as defined above and as amended by any posted notices or oral announcements during the sale) is not substantially correct based upon a fair reading of the catalogue as a whole, including the terms of any Glossary contained herein, the sale of such lot will be rescinded and the original purchase price refunded.

3. Non-Assignability. It is specifically understood that the benefits of this Guarantee are not assignable and shall be applicable only to the original purchaser of the lot from us and not to the subsequent owners or others who have or may acquire an interest therein.

4. Sole Remedy. It is further specifically understood that the remedy set forth herein, namely the rescission of the sale and refund of the original purchase price paid for the lot, is exclusive and in lieu of any other remedy which might otherwise be available as a matter of law.

5. Exclusions. The guarantee covers only the catalogue description of the physical condition and/or authenticity of property as explicitly set forth in 1 and 2 above, and does not extend to (i) any such catalogue description which may be proven inaccurate by means of scientific processes not generally accepted for use until after publication of the catalogue or (ii) the secondary and supplemental descriptive material which appears in each entry in the catalogue and which is not material to the description of physical condition or authenticity (as defined in 2 above) of the lot. Although due care is taken to insure the correctness of said supplemental material, the guarantee does not extend to any possible errors or omissions therein.

2/85 BCS

Guide for prospective buyers

Sotheby's encourages buyers to read through the "Conditions of Sale" and "Terms of Guarantee" which appear on the preceeding pages. The following definitions and explanations are provided for the convenience of prospective bidders.

Reserves

Definition:
A "Reserve" is the confidential minimum price agreed between the seller and us, below which the lot will not ordinarily be sold. On unsold lots, less than the full commission may be paid.

Policy:
All lots marked with □ immediately preceding the lot number are being offered subject to a reserve. Our standard advice to sellers is that reserves be set at a percentage of the mean of the estimates, generally somewhat below the low estimate. In no case do we permit a reserve to exceed the high estimate. Estimates for each lot are printed in the catalogue or may be obtained from the expert department.

Implementation:
We as agent for the seller protect reserves, that is, place bids during the auction if and when the highest outstanding bid at any time during the sale is below the reserve on the lot being offered.

Owned Property

Definition:
"Owned property" is property which, at the time it is offered for sale at auction, is owned solely or partially by us or an affiliate (and in the sale of which we are acting as a principal and not an agent).

Policy:
The purchase of property by us for sale at auction is an insignificant part of our overall business. Direct purchases are only made at the request of a client and, in these cases, only after standard commission sales have been rejected by the client. Reserve prices of property owned by us are set on the same or a lower basis than property sold for other consignors, that is, reserves usually will be set below the low pre-sale estimates provided with this catalogue and in no case will they be higher than the high estimates. All property owned by us will be identified in the catalogue as "Property of Sotheby's" or a similar recognizable designation. In some cases, the prior source of property will be identified, e.g., "Property from the Estate of John Doe sold by order of the present owner Sotheby's."

Implementation:
Bidding by us to protect reserves on property is effected in the same way as bidding to protect reserves on property consigned by an outside seller.

Buyer's Premium

A premium of 10% will be added to the successful bid price of all property sold by us, whether consigned to us or "owned property" as defined above, and whether picked up or delivered, and this premium is payable by all purchasers without exception.

Exportation Permits

Certain property sold at auction by us may be subject to the provisions of the Endangered Species Act of 1973, or the Marine Mammal Protection Act of 1972. In order to export these items, special licenses must be obtained from the Department of the Interior, U.S. Fish and Wildlife Service. There are no assurances that any such license can be obtained. Please contact the appropriate expert department if you have any questions.

Sales Tax

New York State sales tax is charged on any purchases picked up or delivered in New York State, unless the purchaser (regardless of state or country of business) has given Sotheby's a valid exemption issued by New York State. Purchases shipped to Florida, Illinois, Massachusetts, Pennsylvania, Texas, and Washington, D.C. are subject to the sales tax of those states. If you have any questions regarding your sales tax liability, or need assistance in obtaining a New York exemption, please contact our Customer Billing Department at (212) 606-7464 before placing your bids.

Estimates

Sotheby's catalogues provide detailed descriptions and pre-auction estimates for each lot included in a sale. These estimates are guides for prospective bidders and should not be relied upon as representations or predictions of actual selling prices. Estimates are determined well in advance of the sale date and are subject to revision. Please contact the expert in charge of the sale if you have any questions.

Expert Advice

Sotheby's experts and Client Service representatives are available at our pre-sale exhibitions, and by appointment, to advise prospective bidders on particular objects or on any aspect of the auction process.

Currency Conversion Board

For our clients' convenience, a computerized display board, which converts U.S. dollars into a variety of foreign currencies, is operated during some sales. Foreign currency amounts displayed on this board are approximations. While every effort is made to use the latest exchange rate information available, the conversion display is for convenient reference only and is not to be relied upon as a precise invoice amount. We assume no responsibility for any errors or omissions in foreign or U.S. currency amounts shown. The total purchase price and applicable taxes are payable in U.S. dollars only.

Bidding

Bidding at all auctions is by paddle. Please register for your paddle at the entrance to the salesroom. If your bid is successful at the auction, your paddle number will be called out by the auctioneer, or you will be asked to sign a bid confirmation card upon the fall of the hammer. Unless you have previously established credit or made payment arrangements, you will not be permitted to take delivery of your purchases until after your check has cleared. To avoid such delays, you may apply for a Check Acceptance Account before attending your first auction by filling out an application available from our cashier.

Absentee Bids

If you are unable to attend an auction, you may use the "Absentee Bid Form" provided at the back of this catalogue. Following your instructions, Sotheby's will act on your behalf to try to purchase the lot or lots of your choice for the lowest price possible – and never for more than the top amount you indicate. Absentee bidding, a free service handled in strictest confidence by our Bid Department, allows you to participate in any Sotheby's auction worldwide. For more detailed information, see "Guide to Absentee Bidders" at the back of this catalogue or call Roberta Louckx at (212) 606-7414.

Removal of Property

Unless other arrangements have been agreed upon, we must ask buyers to remove their purchases by 5 pm on the third business day following the sale. Purchases not removed within this time will be subject to a handling charge, as outlined in paragraph 7 of the "Conditions of Sale."

The packing and handling of purchased lots by our employees is undertaken solely as a courtesy to our clients, and in the case of fragile articles, will be undertaken only at our discretion. In no event will we be liable for damage to glass or frames, regardless of the cause.

Although we recommend the use of professional packers, books and small articles which are not fragile can be packed on our premises for a nominal charge, and, at our sole discretion, be sent by mail or other carrier. Prints and drawings in glazed frames cannot be handled in this manner.

Sotheby's Art Transport Department and the staff at any of our regional offices can make all the arrangements necessary for shipping purchases to you. There is no charge for this service, but actual shipping expenses and packing and insurance charges are payable by the client. For further information please call Eileen Baral at (212) 606-7511.

Guide for prospective sellers

If you have property you wish to sell at auction, please call the appropriate expert department to arrange for a consultation. (A list of expert departments appears in the front of this catalogue.) If you are unsure which department would handle your property, or if you have a variety of objects to sell, please call one of our general representatives:

Fine Arts Representatives
Michael Owen, (212) 606-7121
Beverly Miller, (212) 606-7120

Decorative Arts Representative
Sarah D. Coffin, (212) 606-7420

Inspection of Property
You may bring your property – or photographs if it is not portable – directly to our galleries where our experts will give you auction estimates and advice. There is no charge for this service, but we request that you telephone ahead for an appointment. Inspection hours are 9:30 am to 5 pm, Monday through Friday.

Our experts will provide a free preliminary auction estimate, subject to a final auction estimate after first-hand inspection, if you send a clear photograph of each item, or a representative group of photographs if you have a large collection. Please be sure to include the dimensions, artist's signature or maker's mark, medium, physical condition, and any other relevant information.

Evaluations of property can also be made at your home. The usual fees for such visits outside of Manhattan are: other New York City boroughs/$100 per half-day; elsewhere in North America/$250 per day. (Travel expenses are additional.) These fees may be rebated if you consign your property for sale at Sotheby's.

Experts from our Beverly Hills office are available for inspection visits in the western United States. For more information please call (213) 274-0340.

Standard Commission Rates
Sellers are charged 10% of the successful bid price for each lot sold for $5,000 or more. A commission of 15% is charged for each lot sold for $1,000 or more but less than $5,000, and 20% for each lot sold for less than $1,000. There is a minimum handling charge of $100 for any lot sold. If your property fails to reach the reserve price and remains unsold, you pay a reduced commission rate of 5% of the reserve figure. The minimum handling charge for any object that does not sell is $75. (For more information about reserves, please refer to "Reserves" in "Guide to Prospective Buyers.")

Shipping Arrangements
Sotheby's Art Transport Department and the staff at any of our regional offices can advise you on the easiest and safest way to have your property delivered to our galleries. This service is free, but actual packing, shipping and insurance charges are payable by our clients. (While we may recommend packers and shippers, we are not responsible for their acts or omissions.) For further information please call Eileen Baral at (212) 606-7511.

Appraisals

Sotheby's Appraisal Company can prepare appraisals for insurance, estate tax, charitable contributions, family division or other purposes.

Appraisal fees vary according to the nature and amount of work to be undertaken but will always be highly competitive. Flat rates can be quoted based on expert time required, value and processing costs. Travel expenses are additional.

We shall be pleased to refund the appraisal fee pro rata if the appraised property is consigned to us for sale within one year after the appraisal is completed. For further information please call (212) 606-7440.

Sotheby's catalogues, price lists and Newsletter

Illustrated catalogues, prepared by Sotheby's experts, are published for all regularly scheduled auctions and may be purchased singly or by annual subscription. (Catalogue subscribers automatically receive *Sotheby's Newsletter* at no additional charge.)

Printed lists of the prices realized at each auction are available at our galleries approximately three weeks following the auction, and are sent directly to catalogue purchasers and subscribers.

Sotheby's Newsletter, published ten times a year, provides an advance calendar of all Sotheby's sales worldwide and full-color photographs of auction highlights. A complimentary copy is available upon request. Annual subscriptions are $10 ($15 overseas).

For more information, or to subscribe to our catalogues or *Newsletter,* ask for our free brochure. Write or call Sotheby's Subscription Department, P.O. Box 4020, Woburn, Massachusetts 01888-4020. Telephone: (617) 229-2282.

PAUL FRANCIS WEBSTER
1907-1984

Paul Francis Webster was one of the most noted lyricists in the music business and collaborated with many of the great composers, including Sammy Fain, Duke Ellington, Hoagy Carmichael, Dimitri Tiomkin, Max Steiner, Bronislaw Kaper, Alfred Newman, John W. Green, Franz Waxman, Rudolph Friml, André Previn and Henry Mancini. In a career spanning more than 40 years he wrote over 500 songs, received a total of 16 Academy Award nominations (winning three Oscars: for "Secret Love" in 1953, for "Love is a Many Splendored Thing" in 1955, and for "The Shadow of Your Smile" in 1965), as well as 20 gold records and numerous other awards.

A native New Yorker, Webster attended New York and Cornell Universities, majoring in journalism and philosophy and then served for three years as a Merchant Marine. He displayed cool indifference to a career in his father's dress manufacturing business and found immediate success as a lyric-writer.

His career as a book collector was as long as that as a lyricist. His first collection of English and American literature was sold by Parke-Bernet on April 28, 1947. Then, being a true enthusiast, he began gathering the books and manuscripts that are being offered in this sale.

In 1971, he published a catalogue of his "small, select library" and his own introduction to that catalogue (reprinted here with a few necessary alterations) best expresses his profound love of books:

This collection of books and manuscripts represents over 600 years of Western thought and culture, ranging chronologically from a *Magna Carta* of c. 1300-80 to John F. Kennedy's *Profiles in Courage* of 1957.

I have selected a representative group of books and manuscripts which have sparked the mind of man.

Here we may find such disparate items as the theologically orthodox Cardinal de Polignac's *Book of Hours* (1540) next to the irreverent Voltaire's *Candide* (1759); the sanguinary Machiavelli's *The Prince*, paradoxically rubbing elbows with the Signers of the Declaration of Independence; or the chiaroscuro elegance of Herrick's *Hesperides* nudging the earthy humor of Fielding's *Tom Jones*.

Letting one's eyes stray along the well-ordered rows, they might pause at the fanciful grotesqueries of Cervantes' *Don Quixote*, only to react in wonder to the sage excursions into human behavior contained in Montaigne's *Essays*, with the arms of Queen Elizabeth. In the realm of fancy, we bask in the outrageous upsidedown world of Lewis Carroll's *Alice's Adventures in Wonderland* only to be brought abruptly back to earth by the bleak, unrelenting neo-realism of Flaubert's *Madame Bovary*.

In one corner of a shelf the eye takes in Isaac Walton's beloved *Angler*, in another, Mary Baker Eddy's *Science and Health*. Two hundred years apart, but close together in intent and both equally good for the soul. Nearby stands Spenser's *Faerie Queene* (1590-1596). And finally, on the bottom shelf, towering like giant redwoods over the surrounding forest – the four tall folios of Shakespeare, in all their majesty, unsophisticated and prime.

Adding warmth to the library are those books which we categorize as association copies – books in which the sentimental value frequently outweighs the intrinsic. Among these – most dearly beloved – is the slender little volume of Sackville's *Poetical Works* once owned by John Keats, signed by him on the title page and dated in his hand 1820, the year preceding his death.

Robert Burns not only loved but was greatly influenced by the work of the poet James Thomson. How rewarding then, to have Burns' own copy of Thomson's *Seasons;* well worn, thumbed, scribbled in and with his signature on the title and with two small marginal sketches.

On the same shelf, is Oliver Goldsmith's *Beauties of Poesy* (2 vols.), a presentation copy from Goldsmith to Capt. Charles Horneck, whose sister Mary was Goldsmith's "Jessamy Bride" and for whom he entertained more than a friend's regard.

Nobody admired Dickens' work more than did the Danish weaver of fairy tales, Hans Christian Andersen. Therefore, it is with understandable pride that we salute the copy of *Pickwick Papers* in which the author has written, "Hans Christian Andersen/ from his friend and admirer/Charles Dickens/London/July 1947."

Rounding out the circle of the sentimental, we cannot overlook the presentation first edition of Hawthorne's *Scarlet Letter* (the William Harris Arnold copy); an autograph transcript of Julia Ward Howes' immortal Battle *Hymn of the Republic;* and last but not least, from the library of George Washington, his own copy (inscribed by him on the title page) of the *Memoirs of the Life of the Late Charles Lee, Esq.*

All in all, a small, select library, living up to Christopher Marlowe's memorable words – "infinite riches in a little room." And what fun it has been, collecting these literary children. "They have been well read, well tended and well loved, these books and now like neatly scrubbed little orphans in their best morocco bibs and tuckers, they are trembling on the brink of new lives." They are going to print.

P. F. W.

The Library of
Paul Francis Webster

WEDNESDAY, APRIL 24, 1985 AT 2 PM

Afternoon Session: lots 1-181

Magna Carta, lot 59

Order of Sale

FIRST SESSION/WEDNESDAY, APRIL 24,1985 at 2 pm
American, English and European Literature, Lots 1-97
Western Illuminated Manuscripts, Lots 98-104
American Historical Documents, Lots 105-181

☐ 1   AUSTEN, JANE. Pride and Prejudice: A Novel. *London: Printed for T. Egerton, 1813*

3 volumes, 12mo. Half-titles (supplied from another copy for vols. I and II, careful glueing along inner margins), small hole in E12 of the second volume, not affecting text, in F gathering of the second volume much of the text transposed onto the opposite pages with p. 116 being unevenly printed causing faintness of a few words, short marginal tear on title and H1 in the second volume, vol. III, N1 with marginal tear not affecting text, some browning and offsetting. Contemporary half green straight-grain morocco, gilt spine; faded and rubbed, some chipping of spines and edges, some wear to joints. Brown morocco-backed folding box

First edition. The work which inspired Scott's famous judgement: "I read again, and for the third time, Miss Austen's very finely written novel of *Pride and Prejudice*. That young lady had a talent for describing the involvements, feelings, and characters of ordinary life, which is to me the most wonderful I have every met with. The big bow-wow I can do myself like any one going; but the exquisite touch, which renders commonplace things and characters interesting from the truth of the description and the sentiment is denied me. What a pity so gifted a creature died so early!" (Grolier, *One Hundred Books famous in English Literature*, 69)

Gilson A3; Keynes 3; Grolier *English* 69; Chapman, *Jane Austen* 3; Sadleir 626; Tinker 202

Provenance: contemporary signature of John Need on titles

$1,800-2,200

☐ 2   BACON, FRANCIS, *Vicount St. Albans*. The Essayes, or Counsels, Civill and Morall... Newly Written. *London: Printed by John Haviland for Hanna Barret, 1625*

4to. The two leaves of the Table of Contents supplied from another copy, manuscript table on the verso of A4, careful repair of inner margin of title, partial stub of cancelled blank A1, lower outer corner of H2 torn affecting rule, marginal repair to Mm1, some browning, mostly marginal. Contemporary calf; upper cover detached, lower joint cracked, very rubbed. Brown calf-backed slipcase

First complete edition (with most of the variants for issue B and the later readings on pp. 269 and 272) and the last to appear in Bacon's lifetime. The dedication reads "I doe now publish my *Essayes;* which, of all my other workes, have been most Current: For that, as it seemes, they come home, to Mens Business, and Bosomes. I have enlarged them, both in Number, and Weight; So that they are indeed a New Worke..."

Gibson 14; Pforzheimer 30; STC 1148

Provenance: signature of Allan Paton on title

$400-600

☐ 3   BEAUMONT, FRANCIS *and* JOHN FLETCHER. Comedies and Tragedies... Never printed before, And now published by the Authours Originall Copies. *London: Printed for Humphrey Robinson... and for Humphrey Moseley..., 1647*

Folio. Engraved frontispiece portrait by William Marshall (trimmed and carefully laid down); marginal tears, some repaired, generally not affecting text except on a few leaves where one letter is affected, soiling, marginal tear on Mm1 affected pagination, some staining, paper weakness causing tears in 7A1 and 7D1. Contemporary blindstamped calf; rebacked, repairs including renewing of endpapers

First edition, second state of the portrait with "Vates Duplex" in fourth line of inscription under the portrait. This edition contained all the previously unpublished plays by Beaumont and Fletcher except the *Wild-Goose Chase,* which was not included since the manuscript had been lost.

Pforzheimer 53 (portrait in first state); Greg pp. 1013-1018; Wing B-1581; Grolier *English* 28

Provenance: with the eighteenth-century signature (crossed through) and bookstamp of Jane Williams. Her copy of Beaumont's *Bosworth-field,* 1629 was sold in the Houghton sale, June 13, 1979, lot 33

$400-600

☐ 4   BOSWELL, JAMES. The Life of Samuel Johnson. *London: Printed by Henry Baldwin for Charles Dilly..., 1791*

2 volumes, 4to. Portrait engraved by James Heath after Reynolds, and 2 engraved plates of facsimiles engraved by H. Shepherd, initial blank in vol. II; marginal tear in L2. Contemporary tree calf; a few scrape marks, vol. I lower joint cracked but firm, a couple of very small wormholes in spine, upper portion of spine of second volume very scraped. Brown morocco-backed slipcases

First edition, with reading "give" on p. 135 and the cancels as usual. A contemporary manuscript note in margin of p. 464 (vol. II) comments on the line "Dr. Johnson's method of conversation was certainly calculated to excite attention and to amuse or instruct (as it happened) without wearying or confusing his company." The note reads "A Friend of mine who heard him converse said that if you heard him from an adjoining Room with the door open you would suppose that he was reading a book."

Pottle 79; Rothschild 463; Grolier *English* 65; Tinker 338

Provenance: signature of Wm. Holmes with a note "Lent to Mr. Carson Oct. Vth, 1795"; bookplate of Blairhame

$1,200-1,800

JANE EYRE.

An Autobiography.

EDITED BY

CURRER BELL.

IN THREE VOLUMES
VOL. I.

LONDON:
SMITH, ELDER, AND CO., CORNHILL.
———
1847.

5

□ 5   [BRONTË, CHARLOTTE.] Jane Eyre. An Autobiography. Edited by
Currer Bell. *London: Smith, Elder and Co. 1847*

3 volumes, 8vo. Half-titles, 32 pp. publisher's advertisements dated Oct.
1847 preceded by an inset fly-title entitled "A Catalogue of Books" dated
June 1845, and followed by a single leaf advertising *The Calcutta Review;*
minor discoloration of a few leaves, some creasing in second volume.
Original claret cloth, decorated in blind on the covers and spines, gilt
lettering; lower inner hinges cracking with separation following titles,
careful repair to spine of first volume, some rubbing and fading. Cloth
folding box

First edition

Parrish *Victorian Lady Novelists* pp. 87-8; Sadleir 346; Ashley I,72; Magee,
D. *Victoria R.I. A Catalogue...* 117; Wolfe 826; Tinker 379; Sterling 75;
Grolier *English* 83

Provenance: with the Abercairny bookplate

$2,000-3,000

□ 6 [BRONTË, CHARLOTTE.] Shirley, A Tale. By Currer Bell. *London: Smith, Elder and Co, 1849*

3 volumes, 8vo. 16 pp. publisher's advertisements at back of first volume dated Oct. 1849; very careful glueing on inner margin of [A] gathering (vol. I), small piece cut from upper free-endpaper of second volume. Original claret cloth with binder's ticket "Westleys & Co" at back; spines uniformly faded, careful repair of spine on first volume, some wear along the lower inner hinges, slight fraying. Red morocco solander case

First edition, with three pages "Opinions of the Press" at the back of the third volume

Parrish *Victorian Lady Novelists* p. 93; Sadleir 348; Ashley I,73; Wise, *Brontë* p. 15; Tinker 382; Sterling 76

$250-400

□ 7 BURNS, ROBERT. Poems Chiefly in the Scottish Dialect. *Edinburgh: Printed for the Author, 1787*

8vo. Subscribers' list, portrait; light spotting. Contemporary paper-backed boards, paper label, uncut; joints stitched, spine worn. Morocco solander case

First Edinburgh edition, with "Boxburgh", "o" for "of" on p. 9 line 2, "tho" on p. 10 line 9, "skinking" on p. 263 line 13

Egerer 2; Roth 556; Tinker 453; Sterling 103; PMM 231 (Kilmarnock edition)

Tipped in is an autograph letter signed in the third person, 2 pages 8vo, n.p., "Friday eve" [early 1795], to Maria Riddell. With integral address leaf to "Mrs W. Riddell Tinwald House"

An important letter, apparently Burns's response to Maria Riddell's first advance to him after their estrangement. One of Burns's closest female friends, herself a poetess, Maria Riddell cooled towards him after he took part in a celebrated drunken scene at her sister-in-law's house in late 1793 or early 1794. From existing evidence their friendship lapsed until Maria sent him a book and a poem early in 1795. This is his response: he thanks her for sending him a book and explains that owing to the exigencies of his work as Supervisor of Excise "he has not that time to spare which is necessary for any Belle-Lettre pursuit; but, as he will, in a week or two, again return to his wonted leisure, he will then pay that attention to Mrs. R – s beautiful song "To thee, lov'd Nith" – which it so well deserves. When "Anacharsis' Travels" come to hand, which Mrs. Riddell mentioned as her gift to the public library, Mr B– will thank her for a reading of it, previous to her sending it to the Library; as it is a book Mr B– has never seen, and he wishes to have a longer perusal of than the regulations of the Library allow... P.S. Mr. Burns will be much obliged to Mrs Riddell if she will favor him with a perusal of any of her poetic pieces which he may not have seen." (Ferguson, *The Letters,* II p. 282)

Provenance: the John L. Clawson-William Andrews Clark, Jr. copy, with bookplates, sold in Clawson's sale at the Anderson Galleries, November 29, 1920, lot 46

$2,000-3,000

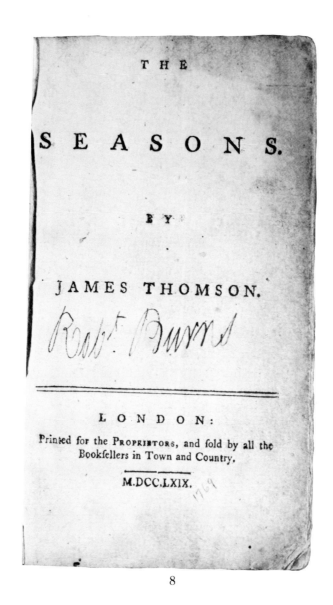

THE

SEASONS.

BY

JAMES THOMSON.

Robt Burns

LONDON:

Printed for the Proprietors, and sold by all the
Bookfellers in Town and Country.

M.DCC.LXIX.

8

☐ 8 [BURNS, ROBERT.] THOMSON, JAMES. The Seasons. *London: Printed for the Proprietors... 1769*

12mo. Occasional spotting, lacking free-endpapers, early pen scribbles on verso of last leaf. Contemporary sheep; rubbed. Morocco solander case

ROBERT BURNS' COPY WITH HIS SIGNATURE ON THE TITLE. "... The poets Burns admired before 1782, and continued to admire later, were didactic and sententious, formal writers for polite readers in England and in Scotland. A great favorite was James Thomson... noted for his long poem, *The Seasons*, in which he drew edifying moral reflections from generalized descriptions of nature; and Alexander Pope, in whom Burns found a source of quotations second only to Thomson." (Fitzhugh, R.T. *Robert Burns, the Man and the Poet,* Boston, 1970, p. 48)

$1,000-1,500

Childe Harold's Pilgrimage.

A ROMAUNT.

——◆——

BY

LORD BYRON.

——————

L'univers est une espèce de livre, dont on n'a lu que la première page quand on n'a vu que son pays.
J'en ai feuilleté un assez grand nombre, que j'ai trouvé également mauvaises. Cet examen ne m'a point
été infructueux. Je haissais ma patrie. Toutes les impertinences des peuples divers, parmi lesquels j'ai vécu,
m'ont réconcilié avec elle. Quand je n'aurais tiré d'autre bénéfice de mes voyages que celui-là, je n'en re-
gretterais ni les frais, ni les fatigues.

LE COSMOPOLITE.

——————

LONDON:

PRINTED FOR JOHN MURRAY, 32, FLEET-STREET;

WILLIAM BLACKWOOD, EDINBURGH; AND JOHN CUMMING, DUBLIN.

By Thomas Davison, White-Friars.

1812.

10

☐ 9 BYRON, GEORGE GORDON, *Lord.* Hours of Idleness. *Newark: Printed and Sold by S & J. Ridge... 1807*

8vo. Half-title, D3 and U2 are cancels, "I1"/"1806" watermark, pp. 167-168 intact, partially unopened; a few marginal tears where roughly opened, light soiling or spotting. Original blue boards; fragments of printed and decorated paper spine, rubbed, soiled. Slipcase

First edition, first issue; with page 171 correctly numbered and the double "where" on page 5 lines 2 and 3

Randolph p. 9; Wise *Byron* I,7-8; Hayward 218; Tinker 507; Sterling 114; Ashley I, 1445; PMM 270

Provenance: contemporary inscription on p. [1]: "Bought by me at Newark on road from my much-loved Country November 18th 1819"

$300-500

□ 10 BYRON, GEORGE GORDON, *Lord.* Childe Harold's Pilgrimage. A Romaunt. [Cantos I-II.] *London: Printed for John Murray... 1812*

4to. Publisher's advertisements at back, plate of facsimile (foxed); light spotting, mostly at back, leaf M2 browned, light waterstain at front. Contemporary russia gilt; upper joint repaired, some rubbing. Brown cloth folding box

PRESENTATION COPY of the first edition of Cantos I and II. Inscribed on blank preceding title by Byron "To Mrs. Dallas with best compliments from the Author". Mrs. Dallas is most likely Sarah Dallas the wife of Robert Charles Dallas whose sister had married Byron's uncle. Dallas was also the friend of Byron who reading *Childe Harold* on Byron's return from Italy was so enthused that Byron allowed him to undertake arranging the publication. At first Dallas was the intermediary between Byron and Murray for this book and the £600 that Byron received for the copyright of the first two cantos was presented to the Dallases. Leaf Bb3 is a cancel with the poem title reading "Written beneath a picture", line 11, p. 97 has had the colon changed to a question mark with pen, first errata entry reads "p. 47"

Randolph p. 19; Wise, *Byron* I, 50; Ashley I, 147; Grolier *English* 68; Tinker 518

Provenance: the A. Edward Newton copy with bookplate, sold at his sale, Parke-Bernet, 17 April, 1941, lot 323

$2,500-4,000

□ 11 [BYRON, GEORGE GORDON, *Lord.*] A Selection of Hebrew Melodies ancient and modern with appropriate symphonies & accompaniments by I. Braham & I.Nathan, the poetry written expressly for the work [by Byron.] [First and Second Numbers.] *London: Published and sold by I. Nathan, [1815]*

2 parts in one volume, folio. Engraved title signed by Braham and Nathan, engraved dedication to the Princess of Wales, engraved music, watermark 1814 in first part and 1815 in second; offsetting, lacking advertisement leaf after page 64, title to the second part is on a stub and trimmed (affects Nathan's signature in lower corner), stubs between pp. 6/7 and 122/3. Later half red morocco

First edition of this format with the music, appearing in April (the DNB saying January). The octavo format of the poems alone appeared June 22, 1815. This is the first appearance of "She Walks in Beauty." "At [Douglas] Kinnaird's suggestion Byron wrote the 'Hebrew Melodies' for [Isaac] Nathan to set to music... He intended to publish the 'Melodies' by subscription, and [John] Braham [the singer], on putting his name down for two copies suggested that he should aid in their arrangement, and sing them in public. Accordingly the title-page of the first edition published in 1815 stated that the music was newly arranged, harmonised and revised by I. Nathan and J. Braham..." (DNB) In 1841 Nathan emigrated to Australia and there continued his musical interests and publications

Tinker 549

Provenance: bookplate of the Apley Library; inscribed on the blank preceding the title of the second part "Caroline Spencer/The gift of Lord Churchi[ll] May 1816"

$250-400

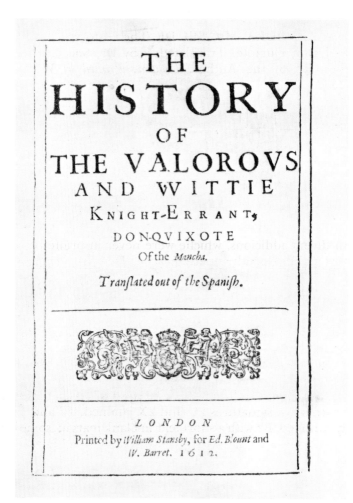

THE
HISTORY
OF
THE VALOROVS
AND WITTIE
KNIGHT-ERRANT,
DON-QVIXOTE
Of the *Mancha.*

Tranſlated out of the Spaniſh.

LONDON
Printed by *William Stansby*, for *Ed. Blount* and
W. Barret. 1 6 1 2.

12

□ 12 CERVANTES SAAVEDRA, MIGUEL DE. The History of the Valorous and Wittie Knight-Errant, Don-Quixote of the Mancha. Translated out of the Spanish [By Thomas Shelton]. *London: Printed by William Stansby for Ed. Blount and W. Barret, 1612*

4to. [ ]⁴, A-Oo⁸, Pp². 7⅛×5⁷⁄₁₆ inches. Some light soiling or staining. Seventeenth-century speckled calf; joints cracking, rubbed. Brown morocco-backed folding box

First edition in English of the first part. This is copy 2 in the census of 17 copies recorded by E. B. Knowles in *PBSA* XXXVII, Third Quarter 1943, p. 207. A good copy of a genuinely rare book

Pforzheimer 140 note; Grolier L-W 213

Provenance: the A. Edward Newton copy sold at his sale, Parke-Bernet, April 17, 1941, lot 346

$8,000-12,000

☐ 13 CERVANTES SAAVEDRA, MIGUEL DE. The History and Adventures of the Renowned Don Quixote. Translated... by Dr. Smollett. To which is Prefixed The Life of the Author. *London: Printed by W. Stratford for J. Stratford, 1811*

2 volumes, 8vo. Handcolored frontispiece, leaf of explanation and 12 handcolored plates; light offsetting. Brown marbled calf gilt by Bayntun, a.e.g.

Appears to be bound from a 36 parts issue

$200-300

☐ 14 CHAUCER, GEOFFREY. The Woorkes of Geoffrey Chaucer, newly printed, with divers addicions, whiche were never in printe before... as in the table more plainly dooeth appere. *London: Jhon Kyngston for Jhon Wight, 1561*

Folio. Black letter, double column, title-page with a woodcut of Chaucer's arms dated 1560, section-titles for "The Canterbury Tales" and "The Romance of the Rose" within a woodcut border (McKerrow 75), woodcut illustration of the knight at head of his tale; first 2 signatures washed, with some minor repairs, and possibly supplied, title-page loose, 4 leaves misbound following A5, lower inner blank margins of signatures B and C repaired, small wormhole in lower blank margins of leaves B1 through K3, lower inner corners of signatures 2U and 2X jammed, T2 and T6 wormed and probably supplied, F2 with a short tear in blank margin, some browning, occasional marginal staining. Eighteenth-century calf-backed boards; repaired

Fifth collected edition, second issue. Edited by John Stowe; the majority of works first added to Chaucer's canon in this edition are spurious

Grolier, L-W 42; Pforzheimer 176 (note); STC 1076

$1,200-1,800

☐ 15 [CLEMENS, SAMUEL L.] The Adventures of Tom Sawyer. By Mark Twain. *Hartford, Conn: The American Publishing Company... 1876*

4to. 4 pp. publisher's advertisements at end; faint waterstain in lower margins at front. Publisher's half brown morocco, gilt and blindstamped, a.e.g.; some rubbing. Brown morocco slipcase

First American edition, first printing, printed on wove paper with frontispiece on p. [iv]. According to the publisher's stock book only 200 copies were bound in half morocco.

BAL 3369

See illustration on next page

$2,500-4,000

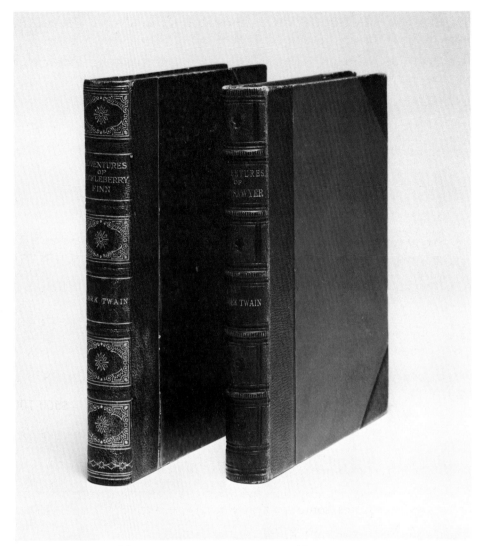

16   15

☐ 16 [CLEMENS, SAMUEL L.] Adventures of Huckleberry Finn (Tom Sawyer's Comrade.) By Mark Twain. *New York: Charles L. Webster and Company, 1885*

4to. Frontispiece portrait, illustrations; light foxing of blanks at back. Publisher's half morocco, marbled boards and edges; slight rubbing. Brown morocco slipcase

First American edition. Portrait frontispiece in state 3 with the imprint of Photo-Gravure Company, not showing the tablecloth and with "Karl Gerhardt, SC" on the finished edge of the shoulder of the bust, the copyright notice dated 1884 and the title apparently conjugate with (1)7, the plate on page 283 in State C, page 13 lists the caption "Him and Another Man" on p. 88, the last "5" lacking in the page number on p. 155, "was" for "saw" on page 57 and with the final blank

BAL 3415

$3,000-5,000

☐ 17 COLERIDGE, SAMUEL TAYLOR. Christabel: Kubla Khan, A Vision: The Pains of Sleep. *London: Printed for John Murray... 1816*

8vo. Half-title; without advertisements, some light spotting. Royal blue morocco gilt by Sangorski & Sutcliffe; slight offsetting from dentelles

First edition

Wise, *Coleridge* 32; Wise, *Two Lake Poets* p. 74; Hayward 207; Grolier *English* 70; Ashley I, 204; Tinker 693

$500-700

☐ 18 COLERIDGE, SAMUEL TAYLOR, PERCY BYSSHE SHELLEY *and* JOHN KEATS. Poetical Works. *Paris: A. and W. Galignani, 1829*

Lg. 8vo. Frontispiece with portrait of the three poets engraved by J.T. Wedgewood on india paper, printed in double column, 8 pp. publisher's advertisements at front, half-title; faint spotting. Original drab boards, paper label (some soiling and chipping); some rubbing. Morocco-backed folding box

First edition of this collection and the first collection of Keats' works

Ashley III, p. 18

Provenance: bookplate of Louise Wart Watkins, and recent ownership signatures

$500-700

☐ 19 [COMBE, WILLIAM *and* THOMAS ROWLANDSON.] Dance of Life. A Poem. *London: Published by R. Ackermann, 1817*

8vo. Handcolored frontispiece and title, 24 colored aquatints; some offsetting from plates, some spotting. Red morocco gilt

Abbey *Life* 264; Tooley pp. 217-8

$250-350

☐ 20 [COMBE, WILLIAM.] The Wars of Wellington, a Narrative Poem. *London: C. Whittingham for the author, 1819*

4to. 30 colored aquatints by W. Heath; plates lightly offset to text, minor foxing. Red morocco gilt, g.e., by Sangorski & Sutcliffe; upper cover detached, joints taped

First edition

Abbey, *Life* 357; Tooley 153

$250-400

☐ 21 CRUIKSHANK, GEORGE. Autograph manuscript, signed several times, 14 pages 4to and 8vo, 10 PAGES BEARING PEN-AND-INK OR WATERCOLOR SKETCHES of soldiers, architectural details etc., the manuscript being a series of notes on the role of the British militia in national defence, perhaps prepared for a letter since one leaf clearly bears the conclusion of a draft letter and is signed "George Cruikshank, Lt. Col. 48th Middlesex Rifles, 263 Hampstead Road, Feby 15th 1867;" some pages written on concluding leaves of letters addressed to Cruikshank by various correspondents. Contained in cloth folder and morocco-backed slipcase

Cruikshank was an enthusiastic militiaman and Lt. Colonel of the Middlesex Rifles, a volunteer regiment

$200-300

☐ 22 [DEFOE, DANIEL.] The Life and Strange Surprizing Adventures of Robinson Crusoe, of York, Mariner. *London, 1719* ☆ The Farther Adventures of Robinson Crusoe; Being the Second and Last Part of his Life. *London, 1719* ☆ Serious Reflections during the Life and Surprising Adventures of Robinson Crusoe: with his Vision of the Angelick World. *London, 1720*

Together 3 volumes, 8vo. With the three engraved frontispieces: Robinson Crusoe by Clark and Pine, folding map of the world in two hemispheres deliniating Crusoe's voyages, folding plate of Crusoe's island by Clark and Pine; first part with signatures [A], X-Aa browned, second part with small marginal loss from R8 not affecting text, marginal tear into final line of text on N1, internal tear in text on U5, and several other leaves with short marginal tears not affecting text, some soiling and staining to all parts especially the second, folding frontispieces slightly creased, frontispiece to first part separating. Contemporary disparate calf, covers of first and second parts blind-panelled, covers of third part with single gilt fillet border, spines similarly gilt in compartments with uniform red and green morocco labels; rubbed, front cover and free endpaper of first part detached. Brown morocco solander case gilt.

First editions, first issues, vol. 1 with title-page and preface in Hutchins' first variant and text on p. 343 in his second variant; vol. 2 in Hutchins' first variant; vol. 3 with catchword on p. 270 in Hutchins' second variant. A fine copy with a distinguished provenance of one of the most popular and influential works of imaginative fiction ever written

Grolier *English* 41; Hutchins, *Robinson Crusoe and Its Printing;* Moore 412, 417, 436; PMM 180

Provenance: signature of original owner, "W Vincent," on free endpaper of first part; Joseph Goodall, bookplate; Beverly Chew, bookplate, sold at Anderson Galleries, December 8, 1924, lot 120; Jerome Kern, bookplate, sold at Anderson Galleries, January 8, 1929, lot 346; Stephen Clark; sold at Parke-Bernet, January 10, 1968, lot 37

See illustration on next page

$10,000-15,000

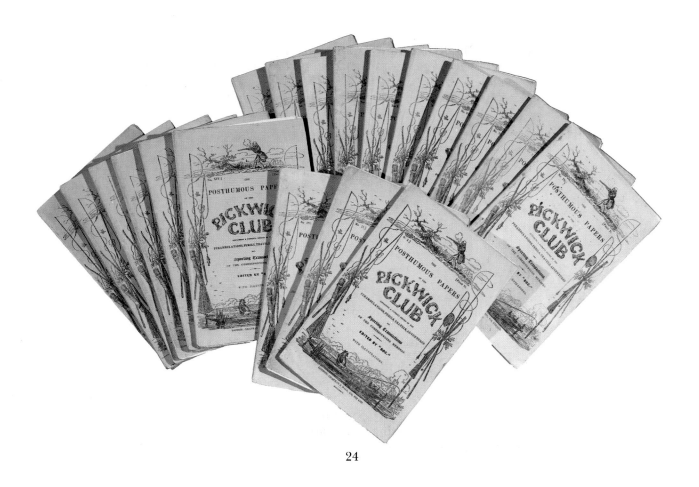

24

☐ 23 DE QUINCEY, THOMAS. Confessions of an English Opium-eater. *London: Printed for Taylor and Hessey... 1822*

12mo. Half-title and publisher's advertisement leaf, uncut; slight browning of endpapers. Original boards; remnants of label, spine defective. Fine red morocco gilt folding box

First edition of the first part of the book, the complete text not appearing until 1850

Tinker 817; Ashley II, 37; Sterling 229

Provenance: signature of J. Mayor on endpaper, also initials J.S.P.

$300-500

□ 24 [DICKENS, CHARLES.] The Posthumous Papers of the Pickwick Club...
Edited by "Boz." *London, 1836-37*

8vo, original 20 monthly parts in 19. Engraved title-page, frontispiece, and 41 plates by R. Seymour (3), R. W. Buss (2), and H. K. Browne ("Phiz"; 38, including 4 after Seymour); plates in part 3 browned but also present in a clean duplicate part lacking some other first issue points, about a third of the other plates with minor marginal discoloration, a few plates and some text leaves with small marginal repairs or closed tears, some faint foxing and marginal soiling, a few leaves in part 16 with red ink blots in bottom blank margin. Original blue-green printed wrappers with pictorial woodcut frame after Seymour, uncut; most parts with extremely skilful spine repair, some with other minor repairs or fraying. Red buckram box gilt

First edition. A NEAR-PRIME "PICKWICK" with most first issue points as recorded by Hatton and Cleaver:
Wrappers: All wrappers are first issue, including those to part 3 with Buss's name as illustrator ("the rarest first issue wrappers of the series," Hatton and Cleaver) and those to part 15 even though dated 1837, excepting four parts with early reprinted wrappers: 1 (Hatton and Cleaver state 19), 2 (state 12), 5 (state 16), and 8 (state 18)
Text: All text is in first state throughout, excepting parts 1, 2, and 10
Plates: All plates are in first state except those in parts 1, 6, 10, and "Mr. Pickwick slides" in part 11; however, first state plates (foxed) for part 6–called by Hatton and Cleaver "the rarest items in the whole realm of 'Pickwick'"–are loosely inserted. The two plates for the text of the final part are those designated the "third" etched by Phiz
Addresses: All seven of the address slips from Dickens and his publishers are present, all save that in part 10 in first state
Advertisements: All issues of "The Pickwick Advertiser" are present except that for part 6, six pages (of 8) of which are loosely inserted. All other advertisements are present, including the first paid ad, "The Toilet," in part 3 and the excessively rare folding sheet for Rowland's Macassar Oil with a woodcut of a black woman in part 5, except the Chapman and Hall slip in part 1, "Phrenology Made Easy" in part 7, "Geo. Henekey, Wine Merchants" in part 8, "Pigot's Coloured Views" in part 13, and the George Mann leaflet in part 9, the last of which Hatton and Cleaver state "cannot be accepted as a definite unit in the construction of part 9" and which is not called for by Eckel or Miller and Strange; two ads are loosely inserted

To summarize, this set of *The Pickwick Papers* comprises 79 of a possible 96 first issue points as recorded by Hatton and Cleaver, and more than half the parts (3-5, 12, 14-19/20) are fully "prime," making this a highly desirable copy of the book that carried Dickens to unprecedented fame as an author, introduced him to the illustrator, Phiz, who would portray most of his characters, and established parts publication as a legitimate format for serious novelists

Eckel, *Prime Pickwicks in Parts;* Grolier *English* 78; Hatton and Cleaver pp. 3-88; Miller and Strange, *A Centenary Bibliography of the Pickwick Papers*

Provenance: Contemporary ownership signatures on front wrappers of parts 6 and 7 ("FSR Villiers 1836"), 9 ("Honbl F Villiers"), and 16 (RH Troude"); this set initially assembled by Thomas Hatton, bibliographer of Dickens; sold in 1936 to Charles S. Langstroth and further perfected by him

See color illustration on previous page

$8000-12,000

22

□ 25   DICKENS, CHARLES. The Posthumous Papers of the Pickwick Club.
London: Chapman and Hall, 1845

8vo. Illustrated; careful repair along inner margins of frontispiece and titles, plates foxed. Contemporary diced russia; rebacked, some rubbing. Red morocco backed slipcase.

PRESENTATION COPY TO "HANS CHRISTIAN ANDERSEN from his friend and admirer Charles Dickens London July 1847". On the 30th of July 1847 Dickens called on Andersen in London and, finding him absent, penned a note and left a parcel of books. These books were nicely bound copies of Dickens' works. Of these volumes twelve are now in the Royal Library, Copenhagen and another is in the Dickens' House; each bears the same inscription as the present volume, as does one at the Free Library of Philadelphia

Provenance: the Barton Currie copy, sold in his sale, Parke-Bernet, May 7, 1963, lot 120

See illustration on next page

$10,000-15,000

THE

Posthumous Papers

OF

THE PICKWICK CLUB.

BY CHARLES DICKENS.

WITH

FORTY-THREE ILLUSTRATIONS, BY R. SEYMOUR AND
PHIZ.

LONDON:

CHAPMAN AND HALL, 186, STRAND.

MDCCCXLV.

72

which was readily granted. With this permission, and the ^shut "door-key, ~~Sam~~ Sam Weller issued forth a ^little before the appointed time, and strolled leisurely towards Queen Square, which he no sooner gained than he had the satisfaction of beholding Mr John Smauker leaning ^his powdered head against a lamp post at a short distance off, smoking a cigar through an amber tube.

26

DICKENS, CHARLES. Autograph manuscript fragment from *The Pickwick Papers,* 1 page 4to, a section from Chapter XXXVII beginning "which was readily granted. With this permission, and the street-door-key, Sam Weller issued forth..." and concluding "Oh that's it, is it" – said Sam "That's...", with six corrections or insertions ranging from one to four words. Small piece of left margin chipped away not affecting text, printer's faint thumb mark. Morocco folder and morocco-backed folding box

MANUSCRIPTS OF DICKENS'S MAJOR WORKS ARE NOW RARELY AVAILABLE FOR SALE. This present leaf was one of twelve from Chapter XXXVII (numbered XXXVI in the manuscript and in the original edition due to the error which had numbered two chapters XXVIII, but renumbered XXXVII in subsequent editions) included in the Suzannet sale in 1971, the last occasion on which significant manuscripts of Dickens works were offered at auction. Only 44 pages of the manuscript of *Pickwick* are known to survive, preserved by Charles Hicks, foreman-printer to the firm of Bradbury and Evans who printed for Chapman and Hall. Apart from the Suzannet leaves, there remain one in Dickens House, six in the British Library, one in the Berg Collection of the New York Public Library and twenty-four in the Rosenbach Foundation; in addition, a four-line fragment was inserted in a copy of *Pickwick* in parts formerly owned by George Ulizio

The chapter from which this leaf is taken is that which "Honorably accounts for Mr Weller's absence, by describing a soiree to which he was invited, and went..." The leaf is numbered 72 in Dickens's hand; Dickens separately paginated his manuscript for each installment of the book as it went to the printer for the publication in parts, and this leaf is page 72 of the manuscript for part XIII

Provenance: Comte Alain de Suzannet, sold in his sale (with eleven other leaves) in our London rooms, November 23, 1971, lot 303

$5,000-8,000

☐ 27 [DICKENS, CHARLES.] Memoirs of Joseph Grimaldi. Edited by "Boz". *London: Richard Bentley, 1838*

2 volumes, 8vo. Portrait frontispiece of Grimaldi by W. Greatbatch after S. Raven, 12 plates by George Cruikshank, 36 pp. publisher's advertisements at back of second volume, half-titles; browning and staining, tear on half-title and free endpaper along inner margin. Original cloth; upper cover of vol. I detached, lower joint cracking, spine of second volume rebacked with original gilt spine laid down, rubbed. Half blue morocco slipcases

First edition

Eckel p. 140

$100-150

☐ 28 DICKENS, CHARLES. [Christmas Books.] A Christmas Carol. *London: Chapman and Hall, 1843,* title in red and blue, half-title in red, yellow endpapers, "STAVE I", original cloth; carefully repaired along spine ☆ The Chimes. *London, 1845,* with the publisher's name in the banner on the vignette title ☆ The Cricket on the Hearth. *London, 1846* ☆ The Battle of Life. *London, 1846,* vignette title in second state ☆ The Haunted Man, *London, 1848,* 2 copies, with variant bindings

Together 6 volumes, 12mo. Illustrated; light soiling. Original cloth; some careful repairs, soiling or rubbing. Red morocco-backed slipcase

First editions, issues as noted

$700-1,200

☐ 29 [DICKENS, CHARLES.] The Life and Adventures of Martin Chuzzlewit... Edited by Boz. *London: Chapman & Hall, 1843-4*

In the original 19/20 parts, 8vo. With slips and advertisements as called for by Hatton & Cleaver, with the "Foreign Travel" slip in part VII and the errata list in Part XIX with 14 lines instead of 13, with the last line of the advertisement on the inner back wrapper of Part XIX/XX reading "A few copies in splendid scarlet binding, adapted to the drawing-room table, or forming an elegant souvenir," plates; light spotting or soiling in a few parts. Original printed wrappers; light soiling, some careful repair to spines, slight fraying. Red morocco slipcase

First edition in parts. The engraved title has the transposed "£" note. This copy is accompanied by an extra copy of Part I with "a" missing from "and" on the bottom line of page 18

Hatton and Cleaver p. 188

$500-700

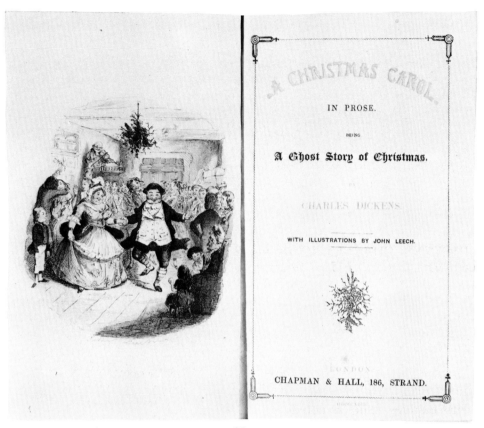

28

☐ 30 DICKENS, CHARLES. A Tale of Two Cities. *London: Chapman and Hall, 1859*

8vo. Engraved title, frontispiece and 14 plates; stitchmarks, some foxing, mostly at front, some short tears along inner margins. Original red cloth; rubbed, soiled, endpapers stained pink. Red morocco-backed slipcase

First edition, bound from the parts issue. With p. 213 misnumbered 113

Eckel p. 86

Provenance: with the bookplates of John Climenson and Myrtle A. Crummer
$150-250

☐ 31 DICKENS, CHARLES. Autograph letter signed, 1 page 8vo, Tavistock House, London, 12 April 1855, to Samuel Phelps. Framed with a portrait

Dickens writes: "I have throughout been quite sensible (and so, I am sure, has Mr. Saunders), that you have done everything you reasonably could to advance the prospects of Love's Martyrdom. Pray believe that throughout the negociations I have not for a moment thought otherwise." The letter refers to the play *Love's Martyrdom* by John Saunders. Dickens admired the piece and having suggested some alterations persuaded Samuel Phelps, the actor-manager of the Sadlers Wells Theatre, to accept it for performance. Negotiations foundered (as evidenced by this letter) and the play enjoyed a run of seven performances at the Haymarket Theatre in June 1855
$300-500

☐ 32 [DODGSON, CHARLES L.] CARROLL, LEWIS. Alice's Adventures in Wonderland. *London: Macmillan, 1866*

8vo. Illustrated by Tenniel; light spotting, cracked along inner hinge following p. 80. Original red cloth gilt, a.e.g.; light soiling and rubbing. Orange morocco gilt box

Second edition, first published English edition, issue with inverted "s" in the last line of the Table of Contents. This copy has dutch blue endpapers rather than the usual dark green and has the binder's ticket "Bound by Burn/ 37 & 38/ Kirby St." on the lower endpaper; the copy also has gilt edges. *The Lewis Carroll Handbook* describes a correction which it has stated was made in 1871, that on page 116, line 6 up from the bottom where the "1870 impression (twenty-fifth thousand) still reads 'the pattern on their back was the same as the rest of their pack': Dodgson wrote on 1 Feb. 1871: for "back" read "backs" and for "their" read "the" (page 30)." The present copy has these corrections, as do other copies of the work with the 1866 title-page which have been compared for this point

PMM 354 note; *The Lewis Carroll Handbook* pp. 32-33

$2,000-2,500

☐ 33 EDDY, MARY BAKER. Science and Health. *Boston: Christian Scientist Publishing Co. 1875*

8vo. Errata leaf; marginal tear on p. 37, light browning and soiling, mostly at front, marginal pencilled notations erased, several gatherings sprung. Original black cloth, blindstamped design; some fraying to head and tail of spine, rubbed. Black morocco-backed slipcase

First edition

PMM 363; Grolier *American, 78*

$500-700

☐ 34 FIELDING, HENRY. The History of Tom Jones. A Foundling. *London: Printed for A. Millar, 1749*

6 volumes, 12mo. Bl (vol. IV) is a cancel, other cancels as usual; some light browning and staining, marginal tear in H2 (vol. II), tear in K2 (vol. II) repaired not affecting legibility, portion of the first gathering sprung (vol. I). Contemporary calf gilt; some cracking or careful repair of joints, new endpaper in front of vol. II, rubbed

First edition

Rothschild 815; Cross III, 316; Grolier *English* 48

Provenance: with the bookplate of the Rev. Henry Leigh Bennett

$700-1,200

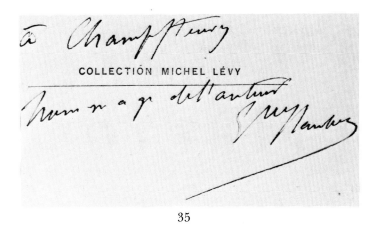

35

☐ 35 FLAUBERT, GUSTAVE. Madame Bovary. Mœurs de Province. *Paris: Michel Lévy Frères, 1857*

2 volumes, 12mo. Half-titles; tears at inner margin of half-title and title of vol. II carefully repaired, affecting two letters on title. Pale blue blindstamped levant morocco, gilt lettering, cream levant doublures and watered silk free endleaves, g.e., by Semet & Plumelle, matching half morocco and marbled paper chemises and marbled open-backed slipcase, original blue printed wrappers bound in; spines of chemises faded

FIRST EDITION, PRESENTATION COPY FROM FLAUBERT TO CHAMPFLEURY, inscribed on half-title of vol. I "A Champfleury hommage de l'auteur G^{ve} Flaubert." A fine association copy, the author of the most famous realistic novel of the nineteenth century sending a copy of his book to Champfleury, the novelist who was at that time regarded as the leader of the realist school. Champfleury is known to have written a letter to Flaubert praising *Madame Bovary*, one of a handful of critics (which also included Sainte-Beuve and Baudelaire) who looked beyond the notoriety attending the publication of the novel and saw it as a work of genius

Vicaire III 721

$4,000-6,000

☐ 36 [FORE-EDGE PAINTINGS.] BYRON, GEORGE GORDON, *Lord.* The Works. *London: John Murray, 1819*

3 volumes, 8vo. Contemporary red straight-grained morocco gilt with gilt and blind-tooled borders, blue watered silk endleaves

DOUBLE FORE-EDGE PAINTINGS on each volume with scenes depicted: 1) Rome and Naples; 2) Como and Florence; 3) Verona and Venice. *Sold as a collection of fore-edge paintings not subject to return*

$1,500-2,000

☐ 37 [FORE-EDGE PAINTING.] OLIPHANT, MARGARET. The Makers of Florence. *London, 1877*

8vo. Purple morocco gilt, with inlay of dutch blue morocco gilt as centerpiece, gilt borders; joints rubbed

With a fore-edge painting of a view of Florence. *Sold as a fore-edge painting not subject to return*

$250-400

THE

DESERTED VILLAGE,

A

P O E M.

By Dr. GOLDSMITH

The sad historian of the pensive plain.

L O N D O N:
Printed for W. GRIFFIN, at Garrick's Head, in Catharine-street, Strand.
MDCCLXX.

42

☐ 38 GOETHE, JOHANN WOLFGANG VON. Faust. Eine Tragödie. *Tübingen: J. Cotta, 1808*

16mo. Somewhat soiled and foxed, cropped close at margins occasionally touching a letter. Contemporary red morocco gilt. Slipcase

First revised edition of the first part of the most famous work in the German language. It was originally published in 1790 as *Faust: Ein Fragment* and then revised. The second part did not appear until 1832

PMM 298 (1834 complete edition)

Provenance: Lilly Library duplicate with release stamp

$300-500

☐ 39　GOLDSMITH, OLIVER. The Traveller, or a Prospect of Society. A Poem. *London: J. Newbery, 1765*

4to. Half-title (carefully repaired), leaf of advertisements; marginal tear on title repaired, G1 marginal tears repaired. Calf gilt by Bedford, open-backed slipcase

First published edition, first issue, of Goldsmith's first poem and first work with his name as author. Samuel Johnson contributed nine lines. There are two trial issues with 1764 on the title

Temple Scott p. 143; Rothschild 1024; I. A. Williams p. 135; Courtney & Nichol Smith p. 113; Tinker 1101; Sterling 399

$400-600

☐ 40　[GOLDSMITH, OLIVER.] The Vicar of Wakefield: A Tale. Supposed to be written by Himself... *Salisbury: Printed by B. Collins for F. Newbery, 1766*

2 volumes, 12mo. Lacking final blank in first volume, marginal tears, some repaired, some text affected, leaves supplied from another copy, some browning. Contemporary calf; repair to upper portion of vol. I spine, careful repair to both spines, some rubbing. Calf-backed box

First edition, Rothschild 1028 variant 3, with a catchword on p. 213, the misprinted catchwords on pp. 71, 75, 77 and 120, and line 20 on page 152 reading "securury"

Temple Scott pp. 173-5; Rothschild 1028; I. A. Williams pp. 136-8; Tinker 1110; Sterling 400; Grolier *English* 53. *Sold with all faults*

$1,000-1,500

☐ 41　[GOLDSMITH, OLIVER.] The Beauties of English Poesy. Selected by Oliver Goldsmith. *London: Printed for William Griffin, 1767*

2 volumes, 12mo. Final blank in first volume and initial and final blanks in second volume are present; final blank in vol. I lacking, some browning, mostly at the back of the second volume, a few short marginal tears. Contemporary calf, gilt spine; light rubbing, repair to upper joint of the first volume, short crack at top of upper joint of vol. I. Rust morocco slipcase

First edition. PRESENTATION COPY inscribed by Goldsmith "From the Authour" and signed underneath by the recipient "C. Horneck" who was Charles Horneck, dubbed by Goldsmith "the Captain in *Lace*" and the brother of Goldsmith's "Jessamy Bride". The Hornecks were close friends of Goldsmith in his later years; according to some reports Goldsmith's feelings for Miss Mary Horneck were more than those of a friend and it was she who at Goldsmith's graveside requested that the coffin be opened so that she might obtain a lock of his hair. With a seven-word note on K4v (vol. I) possibly in Goldsmith's hand. Goldsmith's autograph in any form is very rare

Temple Scott pp. 199-200; I.A. Williams pp. 140-1; Tinker 1117; Sterling 403

Provenance: the John Nash-John Gribbel copy with bookplates, sold at the Gribbel sale Part 4, May 7-8, 1945 lot 206

$4,000-6,000

☐ 42 GOLDSMITH, OLIVER. The Deserted Village, A Poem. *London: Printed for W. Griffin... 1770*

4to. Half-title; several careful marginal repairs not affecting printed area, light soiling. Navy morocco gilt by Riviere

First edition, catchword on p. 9 misprinted "Careless" for "Thus". Published 26 May 1770, this and *The Traveller* were "elegant versions of the popular declamation of the time against luxury and depopulation" (DNB) and in the dedication Goldsmith states "I sincerely believe what I have written; that I have taken all possible pains, in my country excursions, for these four or five years past, to be certain of what I alledge, and that all my views and enquiries have led me to believe those miseries real, which I here attempt to display. But this is not the place to enter into an enquiry, whether the country be depopulating, or not; the discussion would take up much room and I should prove myself, at best, an indifferent politician... In regretting the depopulation of the country, I inveigh against the increase of our luxuries; and here also I expect the shout of modern politicians against me."

Temple Scott pp. 248-50; Rothschild 1032; Hayward 184; Tinker 1122; Sterling 405; Bibliographical Society of University of Virginia, *Studies in Bibliography*, VI, pp. 25-44

Provenance: the Henry Yates Thompson copy with bookplate

See illustration on previous page

$400-600

☐ 43 GOLDSMITH, OLIVER. She Stoops to Conquer, Or the Mistakes of a Night. A Comedy. *London: Printed for F. Newbery, 1773*

8vo. Title, Epilogue and P1 probably supplied, light browning, repairs on F4 not affecting text and L2 affecting some letters. Green morocco gilt by Riviere; faded, joint rubbed

First edition with the price on the title page, upper rule on the title out of alignment, Mm is misprinted "k", p. 65 as "56", from p. 73 onwards numerous pagination errors, epilogue printed on A4r, "Diggory" not included among the "Dramatic Personae", text ends on P1v. Dedicated to Samuel Johnson, with a prologue by Garrick

Temple Scott pp. 301-4; I.A. Williams p. 153; Rothschild 1037; Roscoe, *A Newbery Bibliography* 197; Sterling 408

$500-700

A N

E L E G Y

WROTE IN A

Country Church Yard.

LONDON:
Printed for R. Dodsley in *Pall-mall*;
And sold by M. Cooper in *Pater-noster-Row.* 1751.
[Price Six-pence.]

44

☐ 44 GRAY, THOMAS. An Elegy Wrote in a Country Church Yard. *London: Printed for R. Dodsley... 1751*

4to. Light soiling of title and last leaf, careful marginal repairs to title. Green morocco by Riviere

First edition, first printing with line 4, page 10 reading "hidden Spirit", later corrected to "kindred spirit", with the "S" of "FINIS" partly punched through the paper and the last letter of the catchword on p. 9 in alignment. The poems were published the 16th of February 1751, the publication having been rushed at Gray's entreaty to precede the pirated publication in "The Magazine of Magazines".

Northrup 492; Rothschild 1056; Hayward 173; Ashley II 159; Grolier *English* 49; Tinker 1165; Hazen, *Horace Walpole* 41; Illustrated in Currie's *Fishers of Books*

Provenance: the Barton Currie copy, sold in his sale, Parke-Bernet Galleries, May 7, 1963, lot 178

$7,000-10,000

45

☐ 45　HAWTHORNE, NATHANIEL. The Scarlet Letter, a Romance. *Boston: Ticknor, Reed, and Fields, 1850*

8vo. 4 pp. publisher's advertisements dated March 1, 1850 at front. Original brown cloth; carefully recased, endpapers repaired in the area of the hinges, some light staining of endpaper and of corners of binding. Brown morocco solander case

PRESENTATION COPY, inscribed on endpaper by Hawthorne to David Roberts, a Salem lawyer who was one of Hawthorne's card-playing friends from earlier days. Hawthorne had nicknamed him "Chancellor"

Clark A16.1; BAL 7600; Grolier *English* 90; Grolier *American* 59

Provenance: the William Harris Arnold copy with his bookplate

$3,000-5,000

☐ 46　HENRY VIII, *King of England 1509-1547*. Document signed ("Henry rex"), 5½ × 8½ ins., Greenwich, 3 March 1513, on vellum with papered seal. Tipped onto a sunken mount and contained in a leather folding case

A handsome document authorizing "our trusty and welbeloved servt John Dauncy" to dispense from funds assigned to "the promotion of our Warres" the sum of £ 14 13s 6d to the crossbowmaker Guyllam Cream for making twenty crossbows. To the left of the seal is Cream's receipt for the money, written by a clerk and signed by him with his mark in the shape of a crossbow

$2,500-3,500

47

□ 47 HERRICK, ROBERT. Hesperides: or, the Works both Humane & Divine of Robert Herrick Esq... *London: Printed for John Williams and Francis Eglesfield... 1648*

8vo. Engraved portrait frontispiece by William Marshall (very skilful restoration); washed, some soiling, some manuscript marginalia cropped. Red morocco gilt by Riviere

First edition

Pforzheimer 468; Hayward 95; Grolier W-P 441; Wing H 1595; Biblio. Anglo Poetica 340; Grolier *English* 29; Tinker 1212; Sterling 476

$6,000-9,000

NAPOLEON AT THE SANGUINARY BATTLE ON THE BRIDGE OF LODI.

48

□ 48   IRELAND, SAMUEL. The Life of Napoleon Bonaparte. *London: Vols. I-III John Fairburn, Vol. IV John Cumberland, 1823-25-27-28*

4 volumes. 8vo. Half-titles to vols. I and II, engraved titles to each vol., with the rare printed titles to vols. I and II, the printed title to vol. III apparently supplied (lacks imprint on verso called for by Abbey), 24 colored aquatint plates and three uncolored plates by George Cruikshank; some browning of text and occasional light foxing. Blue morocco gilt, Napoleonic emblems on spines, t.e.g., by Root & Son

The Cumberland issue with the editor's preface in the later state. The first three volumes were published by Fairburn whose imprint appears on all but three of the plates. Cumberland took over the enterprise and issued the fourth volume together with the four engraved title-pages. The Directions to the Binder in vol. IV call for the printed titles to vols. I, II and III to be discarded, hence their scarcity

Abbey, *Life* 359; Tooley 278

Provenance: the Barton Currie copy, sold in his sale, Parke-Bernet, May 7, 1963, lot 212

$800-1,200

☐ 49 [IRVING, WASHINGTON.] A History of New York... by Diedrich Knickerbocker. *New York: Published by Inskeep & Bradford, 1809*

2 volumes, 12mo. With final blank in second volume, folding plate of New Amsterdam frayed affecting imprint and description, short tears along fold, tear into plate repaired, strengthening along inner margin of title applied to secure plate, browning and some staining, lower corners of Q1 and 3 torn not affecting text. Brown calf by Sangorski & Sutcliffe

First edition

BAL 10098; Grolier *American* 28; Grolier *English* 67; Langfeld & Blackburn p. 11

Provenance: Contemporary signature of Sam F. Dawes on title

$200-300

☐ 50 [JOHNSON, CHARLES.] Chrysal; or the Adventures of a Guinea... By an Adept. *London: Printed for Samuel Richards and Co, 1822*

3 volumes, 12mo. 12 handcolored plates; foxing. Boards, original paper labels (soiled), uncut. Red morocco folding box

Second edition. The popularity of this title has been attributed to its thinly veiled allusions to current scandals. The key to the characters can be found in Davis's *Olio*

Tooley 283

$100-150

☐ 51 JONSON, BEN. The Workes of Beniamin Jonson... *London: Printed by William Stansby, 1616*

Folio. Engraved title by William Hole; light soiling, marginal repairs, A4 repaired into text with the loss of several words, 3L2 repaired into text but text legible, last two leaves soiled and washed (?supplied), lacks initial blank. Red morocco gilt by Pratt; some rubbing of joints, inner corner of upper cover knocked

LARGE PAPER COPY of the first edition. The engraved title is in Pforzheimer state 3, the title of "Every Man..." not in a border and reads "London: Printed by William Stansby, MDCXVI", and "Cynthia's Revels" title page is not within border

Pforzheimer 559; NSTC 14751; Greg III 1070-3; Grolier *English* 17

Provenance: notation on blank preceding title "Margaret Cavendishe Harley, given me by my Father, July 13, 1732 Wimpole" and note on endpaper "Perfect-R.H. Johnston Collated 13 March 1869"; with an unidentified leather bookplate at front and back

$2,500-4,000

John Keats
1820

THE

POETICAL WORKS

OF

THOMAS SACKVILLE,

LORD BUCKHURST AND EARL OF
DORSET;

CONTAINING

GORBODUC,

AND

INDUCTION AND LEGEND OF HENRY DUKE OF BUCKINGHAM.

In vain I think, right honorable lord,
By this rude rhyme, to memorize thy name,
Whose learned Muse hath writ her own record
In golden verse, worthy immortal fame.   SPENSER.

LONDON:
C. CHAPPLE, 66, PALL MALL, BOOKSELLER TO
THE PRINCE REGENT.
1820.

55

☐ 52   JONSON, BEN. The Works… which were formerly printed in two volumes
are now reprinted in One to which is added a Comedy called the New Inn.
With Additions never before Published. *London: Printed by Thomas Hodgkin,
for H. Herringman… 1692*

Folio. Portrait frontispiece; browned, some staining, burn holes affecting a
word on Kk1 and Oo1, hole on 5B1 affecting a word and tear along upper
margin of 5C2, marginal repair to title, some fraying of fore-edges. Old calf;
repaired and rebacked

First complete collected edition

Pforzheimer 56; Wing J1006

$100-200

□ 53   KEATS, JOHN. Endymion. A Poetic Romance. *London: Printed for Taylor and Hessey, 1818*

8vo. Without advertisement leaves or half-title, faint spotting of some leaves. Green morocco by Sangorski & Sutcliffe, ornately tooled in gilt and blind with gilt urn on upper cover and gilt lyre on lower cover, spine gilt; slight fading

First edition, first issue with the 1-line errata leaf and the 5-line errata slip. Keats' second book

MacGillivray p. 4; Hayward 232; Ashley III 13; Tinker 1419; Sterling 522

$600-800

□ 54   KEATS, JOHN. Lamia, Isabella, the Eve of Saint Agnes and Other Poems. *London: Printed for Taylor and Hessey, 1820*

12mo. Publisher's advertisements at the back; wanting the half-title, some soiling and foxing, some short marginal tears where unevenly opened. Rust morocco gilt

First edition of Keats's last book

MacGillivray p. 5; Hayward 233; Grolier *English* 72; Ashley III, pp. 15-16; Tinker 1420; Sterling 523

$600-900

□ 55   [KEATS, JOHN.] SACKVILLE, THOMAS. The Poetical Works. *London: C. Chapple, 1820*

12mo. Half morocco; spine rather faded, slight rubbing of extremities, front free endpaper coming loose. Morocco-backed slipcase

JOHN KEATS'S COPY WITH HIS SIGNATURE "JOHN KEATS 1820" ON TITLE-PAGE; ONE OF TWENTY-SIX BOOKS FROM KEATS'S LIBRARY NOW KNOWN TO EXIST.

In Keats's informal will, written on a scrap of paper and attached to his letter to John Taylor of August 14, 1820, he ordered "My chest of books divide among my friends". This wish was executed by his friend Charles Brown who distributed some eighty-one titles among eighteen of Keats's friends. Frank N. Owings, Jr., in his study of Keats's library, locates twenty-five works, mainly poetry. In an appendix he lists this volume and one other work which have passed through the auction rooms but whose whereabouts he was unable to determine; neither was contained in his "chest of books". The appearance of this volume of Sackville's poetry is a pleasing addition to the works of Shakespeare, Dante, Chaucer, Jonson, Milton, Ovid and Spenser which survive in the copies that Keats himself owned and read

Frank N. Owings, Jr., *The Keats Library*. London: The Keats-Shelley Memorial Association, n.d. p. 63

Provenance: Thomas J. McKee, with bookplate, sold at his sale, Anderson Galleries, May 12, 1902, lot 5182 ($460); George G. Tillotson, of Wilkes-Barre, PA, sold at his sale, Anderson Galleries, February 1, 1910, lot 315 ($260); William Harris Arnold, title-page reproduced in his *Ventures in Book Collecting*, New York, 1923, pp. 27-28 where Arnold claims to have bought the book at the McKee sale. Owings surmises that Arnold was mistaken and actually made the purchase at the Tillotson sale. The book was not included in Arnold's sale at the Anderson Galleries, November 2, 1924

$8,000-12,000

☐ 56 LOCKE, JOHN. An Essay Concerning Humane Understanding. In Four Books. *London: Printed by Eliz. Holt for Thomas Basset... 1690*

Folio (329 × 185 mm.). Some light spotting or soiling. Contemporary calf; very rubbed. Brown cloth folding box

First edition, first issue with the "Eliz. Holt" imprint, the "SS" in "Essay" aligned and the dedication undated

Pforzheimer 599; Grolier *English* 36; Wing L2737; PMM 164

Provenance: contemporary signature of T. Willoughby on the title, probably Sir Thomas Willoughby, the second Baronet, later Baron Middleton; sold in the Wollaton Library Sale at Christie's, June 15-18, 1925, lot 553

$5,000-8,000

☐ 57 LORSCH GOSPELS. *New York: Braziller, 1967*

Folio. Four- and two-color reproduction of the original manuscript. Original vellum-backed cloth, publisher's box

Limited to 1000 copies. A facsimile of the magnificent Carolingian manuscript, the two parts of which are preserved in the Biblioteca Documentara Batthyaneum in Alba Julia, Rumania and in the Biblioteca Apostolica Vaticana respectively. The separate pamphlet containing an introductory text and colored engravings is not present with this copy

$100-150

☐ 58 MACHIAVELLI, NICCOLO. Nicholas Machiavel's Prince. Also The Life of Castruccio Castrancani of Lucco and the Meanes Duke Valentine us'd to put to death Vitellozzo Vitelli, Oliverotto of Fermo, Paul and the Duke of Gravina. Translated out of Italian into English by E[dward] D[acres]. With some Animadversions noting and taxing his errours. *London: Printed by R. Bishop for Wil: Hils and are to be sold by Daniel Pakeman... 1640*

12mo. A⁶, B-O¹². Printed within rule; small burnhole on fore-edge affecting the rule of a few pages, some soiling of title, endpapers and fore-edges. Contemporary sheep, double fillet ruled in blind on covers; careful repair to spine, some rubbing along edges and joints. Red morocco slipcase

First edition in English. "This famous book is an analysis of the methods whereby an ambitious man may rise to sovereign power. It is the perfect statement of the ruler's task in the 16th century. The lack of scruple which is traditionally associated with it is but one side of a work in which for the first time the practical is paramount to the theoretical. Directed to the unification of Italy, the main theme is that with such a goal in view, all means to attain it are possible and legitimate. It is the work of a great political thinker with an equally clean insight into the facts. Immensely popular in its own time, it influenced the politicians of the European Renaissance, and its influence continues to this day." (Webster 67 note)

NSTC 17168; Newberry Check List of Courtesy Books 930

$800-1,200

AN
ESSAY

CONCERNING

Humane Understanding.

In Four BOOKS.

Quam bellum est velle confiteri potius nescire quod nescias, quam ista effutientem nauseare, atque ipsum sibi displicere ! Cic. de Natur. Deor. *l.* 1.

LONDON:

Printed by *Eliz. Holt*, for **Thomas Basset**, at the *George* in *Fleetstreet*, near St. *Dunstan's* Church. MDCXC.

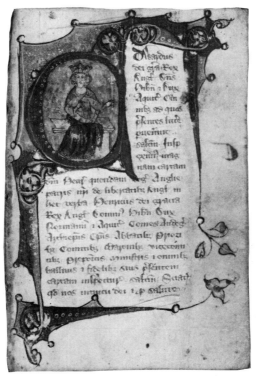

59

□ 59   MAGNA CARTA and the Statutes of England, in Latin and French. *England, probably Yorkshire, c. 1300-1325*

ILLUMINATED MANUSCRIPT ON VELLUM (4×2⅞ in.; 100×72 mm.), 182 leaves (6 blank) plus 9 medieval flyleaves, complete, gatherings mostly of 8ll. (xiv⁶) with some traces of catchwords, 22 lines, written in brown ink in a small charter hand, headings in gothic script, some on-line initials in blue or gold, paragraph-marks around chapter numbers and running-titles in blue or burnished gold, Calendar in red, blue and brown, preliminary tables of chapters with paragraph-marks in red and blue, TWENTY-FIVE ILLUMINATED INITIALS (4- and 9-line, mostly 5- to 7-line) in leafy and floral designs in blue, pale green, red-brown, orange, and burnished gold, with white tracery, and with full-length borders with leafy extensions around upper and lower margins, LARGE HISTORIATED INITIAL (11-line) with branching leaf border extending into four margins, some rubbing and signs of use, some smudging and offsetting, some marginal stains, generally sound, LATE MEDIEVAL BINDING of calf over wooden boards sewn on 3 thongs pegged into the boards, blind ruled in panels with lattice design in central compartment, metal clasp and catch, binding worn and partly defective, in a black morocco slipcase, title gilt

Provenance:(1) Written for use in Yorkshire: the Calender singles out as double feasts in blue SS.Wilfred of York (24 April and 10 October) and John of Beverley (7 May, and his translation on 25 October) and the feast of relics on 19 October. John of Beverley (d.721), archbishop of York, was not entered in the Sarum Calender until 1416 and therefore his feast here is of local observance. (2) A few words in shorthand on f.181 are probably in the same hand as the date 1649 added on f.10. (3) Joseph Waldron, with signature on f.180. (4) Soame Jenyns (1704-1787, author), with his signature on f.23

Text: The Statutes, in French and Latin, form the earliest type of secular manuscript produced in any quantity in England, and the present copy falls within the first generation of these books. Many of them were made for lawyers and can be associated with the Inns of Court in London. The present book must have been made for a lawyer or administrator in Yorkshire, perhaps York itself. The copy of Magna Carta here is dated 23 March 1300 (28 Edward I) and is therefore within a quarter of a century of the great charter itself

The texts here are: Calender (f.2); tables of chapters (f.10); MAGNA CARTA in the form of the Inspeximus of Edward I, *Statutes of the Realm*, I, 1810, pp. 38-41 (f.25); the Forest Charter, *Statutes*, I, pp. 42-4 (f.35); the Statute of Merton, *Statutes*, I, pp. 1-4 (f.41); the Statute of Marlborough, *Statutes*, I, pp. 19-25 (f.46*b*); the Statute of Gloucester, in French, *Statutes*, I, pp. 45-50 (f.61); the First Statute of Westminster, in French, *Statutes*, I, pp. 26-39 (f.68); the Second Statute of Westminster, *Statutes*, I, pp. 71-95 (f.97); the Third Statute of Westminster (f.152*b*); De Conspiratoribus, *Statutes*, I, p. 216 (f.154); Champartour (f.154*b*); De Mercatoribus, *Statutes*, I, pp. 98-100 (f.155*b*);Circumspecte Agatis (f.161); De Vocatis ad Warentum, *Statutes*, I, p. 108 (f.162); De Wardis et Releviis, *Statutes*, I, p. 228 (f.164); Visus Franciplegii, *Statutes*, I, p. 246 (f.165*b*); Articuli contra Prohibitionem Regiam, *Statutes*, I, p. 101 (f.167); Calumpnia Essonia, *Statutes*, I, pp. 217-8 (f.168*b*); Homagium et Fidelitatem, *Statutes*, I, p. 227 (f.169*b*); Quatuor Modus dicitur Exceptio (f.170*b*); De Bigamis, *Statutes*, i, p. 42 (f.171*b*); De Sokage et eius Natura, as in BL.Royal MS.10.A.VI, art. 30 (f.173*b*); De Religiosis, *Statutes*, I, p. 51 (f.174*b*); the Provisions of Windsor (f.176); Articuli Wyntonie (f.176*b*); De Ponendis in Assisis et Iuris (f.178); and Dies Communes in Banco, *Statutes*, I, p. 208 (f.179)

Illumination: English secular art of the early fourteenth century is not common. The miniature on f.25 shows Edward I (who died in 1307) seated on a bench and crowned and holding a sceptre, against a background of a semé of fleurs-de-lys. Probably it was intended to paint a second miniature in the initial on f.35 as the central compartment has been left blank

$7,000-10,000

☐ 60   MAGNA CHARTA, Cum statutis quae antiqua vocantur, iamtecens excusa, & sunna side emendata, justa vetusta exemplatia ad Parliamenti rotulos examinata: *[London]: Richard Tottell, 1556*

2 parts in one volume, sm. 8vo. Browning and staining, manuscript marginalia. Old calf; rebacked

NSTC 9278

$250-400

☐ 61   [MAGNA CARTA.] THOMSON, RICHARD. An Historical Essay on the Magna Charta of King John: To which are added, the Great Charter in Latin and English... *London: Printed for John Major... 1829*

8vo. Text within decorative border; cracking along hinge following frontispiece and preceding last leaf of text, light soiling. Later half calf; rubbed, some chipping of spine

$80-120

☐ 62   MARKHAM, EDWIN. The Man with the Hoe and Other Poems. *New York: Doubleday & McClure Co, 1899*

8vo. Original green cloth; slight rubbing of corners or spine. Red morocco-backed folding box

PRESENTATION COPY: "My dear Luther M. Cornwall: Here is the book of my youth signed in the hours when the shadows are lengthening toward the east. March 18. 1923". First collected edition

$200-300

☐ 63   MAUPASSANT, GUY DE. Des Vers. *Paris: G. Charpentier, 1880*

12mo. Half-title; foxing, mostly affecting first three leaves. Blue morocco-backed boards

First edition of Maupassant's only book of verse, PRESENTATION COPY to the Baron de Vaux, inscribed on half-title "A mon ami le baron de Vaux son camarade Guy de Maupassant." A fine association copy, presented by Maupassant to one of his models for the character of Bel-Ami. The Baron de Vaux (whose title was almost certainly bogus) was a former fencing master and in charge of the gossip column for *Gil Blas*, the light and rather scandalous Parisian newspaper for which Maupassant began to write at about the time of the publication of *Des Vers*. Together with his assistant who was known as the "intrepid bottle-opener," Vaux not only reported on the activities of the *haute* and *demi-monde* but had a profitable side-line in the training and launching of expensive courtesans. *Gils Blas* and the *Gaulois*, another paper to which Maupassant contributed, certainly provided the setting for the novel *Bel-Ami* and Vaux is sometimes credited with being Maupassant's chief model for the title character

Vicaire V 605

$600-800

☐ 64   MELVILLE, HERMAN. Moby Dick; or, the Whale... *New York: Harper & Brothers, 1851*

8vo. 6 pp. publisher's advertisements at back, 5 pp. of which advertise Melville's other works and the last page Harper's publications; foxing throughout as usual. Original brown cloth, sides stamped in blind with a heavy rule border and the Harpers circular device in the center, gilt lettering on spine with decorative gilt rules at head and tail, orange coated endpapers; some fraying or chipping at head and tail of spine, faint discoloration, light rubbing

First American publication, shortly following the three volume English edition, *The Whale*. There exist some differences in the text between the two editions as Bentley edited the English edition (without Melville's knowledge). Most of the editing related to toning down profane and irreverent expressions and omitting the epilogue. This last was said to have "caused at least one English review to comment on the impossibility of a first person narrative, when everyone on the *Pequod* was killed by the white whale's attack" (Grolier *American* p. 93)

Provenance: pencilled signature of Mrs. L.G. Thomson Whirling [?] on endpapers and title

$3,000-5,000

Paradiſe loſt.

A

P O E M

Written in

T E N B O O K S

By *JOHN MILTON*.

Licenſed and Entred according
to Order.

L O N D O N

Printed, and are to be ſold by *Peter Parker*
under *Creed* Church neer *Aldgate*; And by
Robert Boulter at the *Turks Head* in *Biſhopſgate-ſtreet*;
And *Matthias Walker*, under St. *Dunſtons* Church
in *Fleet-ſtreet*, 1667.

65

□ 65 MILTON, JOHN. Paradise Lost. A Poem Written in Ten Books. *London: Printed, and are to be sold by Peter Parker... 1667*

Sm. 4to. Lacking initial blank, neatly washed, browned, upper edge of title trimmed. Claret morocco by Riviere, gilt and blind tooled, a.e.g., light rubbing

First edition, "first title-page" with Milton's name in full and in larger type than "London"

Pforzheimer 716; Hayward 72; Grolier W-P II, 187; Grolier *English* 33; Amory Ib II

Provenance: The C.W. Clark-Silver copy

$10,000-15,000

☐ 66　MILTON, JOHN. Paradise Regain'd. A Poem in IV Books. To which is added Samson Agonistes. *London: Printed by J.M. for John Starkey... 1671*

8vo. License leaf (slightly smaller than title), errata leaf; tear on title carefully repaired not affecting legibility of text, title of "Samson" (I1) supplied in facsimile (possibly also K8), I8 glued along gutter to I7, light spotting or soiling. Nineteenth-century calf labeled "Plays Vol. 59"; other contents removed and blanks inserted, recased

First edition, with "loah" on p. 67

Grolier W-P 616; Hayward 73; Wing M 2152

Provenance: signature of Tho. Rundall on verso of license leaf; the Chatsworth copy with Devonshire bookplate and label on spine; Huntington Library duplicate. *Sold with all faults*

$200-300

☐ 67　MONTAIGNE, MICHEL DE. The Essayes Or Morall, Politike and Millitarie Discourses of Lo: Michaell de Montaigne... *London: Printed... by Val[entine] Sims for Edward Blount... 1603*

Folio. Translated by John Florio, 2 pp. errata at end, Qq4 blank; title soiled, washed, careful marginal repairs, 3G4 with small burn hole affecting a letter, soiling and light browning. Old calf with the arms of Elizabeth I in gilt on the covers; careful repairs and rebacking, endpapers renewed. Red morocco solander case

First edition in English

Pforzheimer 378; Grolier L-W 102; NSTC 18041; PMM 95 (the 1580 edition)

Provenance: the Rev. Philip Bliss copy with his mark on B1; pencilled note on blank preceding title "This volume belonged to the library of Cro--- Ferguson and was purchased at the Sale of his books in 18-- by John Scott price £0.7 (Sotheby's)"

$3,000-4,000

☐ 68　POE, EDGAR ALLAN. Tales of the Grotesque and Arabesque. *Philadelphia: Lea and Blanchard, 1840*

2 volumes, 12mo. 4 pp. advertisements containing "Opinions" of this work; light foxing, mostly of endpapers, cracking before title of second volume. Original purple muslin, paper label (worn); fading and rubbing. Purple morocco-backed slipcase

First edition with p. "213" misnumbered "231" and the "i" in "ing" below the line. One of 750 copies

BAL 16133; Heartman & Canny (1943) p. 49

Provenance: Signature of M.T. Willard in each volume

$800-1,200

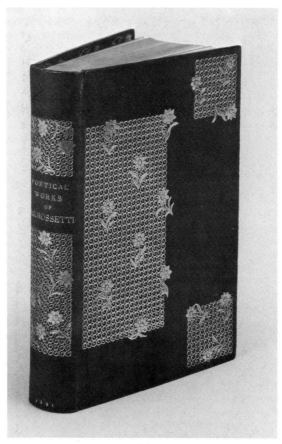

70

☐ 69   RICHARDSON, HENRY HANDEL. Richard Mahonys Skaebne. *Copenhagen: H. Hagerup, 1931,* 2 volumes, mostly unopened, original printed wrappers (some fading and fraying), with a 2-page ALs to Paul Lemperly laid in ☆ Ultima Thule being the Third Part of the Chronicle of the Fortunes of Richard Mahony. *London: William Heinemann, 1929,* first edition, original black cloth, dust-jacket, with a 1-page ALs to Paul Lemperly

Together 3 volumes, 8vo. Faint browning

PRESENTATION COPY of the first work, "To Jacob Schwartz- A much abridged Version of the Trilogy Henry Handel Richardson." Signed in the second volume by Richardson. The classic trilogy of Australian life

$300-400

☐ 70   ROSSETTI, DANTE GABRIEL. The Poetical Works. *London: Ellis and Elvey, 1895*

12mo. Half-title, engraved frontispiece portrait. Dutch blue morocco, elaborately gilt in imitation of the original cloth binding, dentelles gilt with scattered floral tools, g.e. by Zaehnsdorf; slightest rubbing of joints

Tipped in is an autograph letter signed ("DGR"), 1 page 8vo., 16 Cheyne Walk, n.d., to Hayden, presumably Samuel James Bouverie Hayden, the sculptor turned print-seller with whom Rossetti became friendly in later years

$350-500

☐ 71 ROWLANDSON, THOMAS *and* [WILLIAM COMBE.] The Second Tour of Doctor Syntax, in Search of Consolation; a Poem. *London: R. Ackermann, 1820*

In the original 8 parts, 8vo. 24 colored aquatints, leaf of Directions to the Binder, advertisements in parts 3, 4 and 8 as called for by Abbey. Original printed wrappers, uncut; lacks wrappers to parts 6 and 8, advertisements in wrappers to parts 1 and 2 differing from those described by Abbey, wrapper to part 1 darkened and defective with missing portions of text supplied in facsimile, a few minor repairs to other wrappers with some fraying of edges. Morocco-backed box

First edition of the second volume of Combe's celebrated trilogy of satirical poems on English life, written to accompany Rowlandson's witty illustrations. The "Skimmington Riders" plate is in the second state which Abbey claims is never found in copies issued in parts; there is no indication however that part 8 of this copy, containing that plate, has ever been bound

Abbey, *Life* 266

$200-300

☐ 72 [SCOTT, *Sir* WALTER]. Ivanhoe; A Romance. *Edinburgh, 1820*

3 volumes, 8vo. Vol. 1 with final leaf separating, vol. 2 with leaves H6 through I1 with four small impressions poked in them affecting 2 letters, vol. 3 a bit shaken and lacking final leaf of ads. Original boards, backed with sheep, remnants of original paper labels laid down rubbed, spines worn and lacking portions at heads and feet

First edition. The author of *Waverley* marked his greatest popular success with *Ivanhoe*

Grolier *English* 71; Van Antwep, p. 109; Worthington 8

Provenance: lending library labels on front paste-downs; signature of J. Patteson on free endpapers; the Jerome Kern copy, with bookplate, sold at Anderson Galleries, January 22, 1929, lot 1038

$200-300

□ 73 SHAKESPEARE, WILLIAM. Comedies, Histories, & Tragedies. *London, 1623*

Folio (13 × 8½ in.; 330 × 208 mm.). Engraved portrait of Shakespeare by Martin Droeshout on title (in intermediate state between Hind II and III), woodcut capitals and ornaments; title and facing leaf of verses by Ben Jonson very skilfully restored without loss, f1-2 washed and possibly supplied from another copy, about forty words on 2d3 very skilfully restored from another genuine copy, lower forecorner of 3a6 very skilfully restored with the catchword lost and with short bits of the border-rules supplied with pen and ink, the lower forecorners of about the first fifty leaves dampstained chiefly in the margins and neatly strengthened or mended without loss, the gutters of the same leaves often neatly strengthened near the top without loss, about ten tiny rust-holes and about fifteen natural paper faults affecting altogether about fifty letters, few splits, marginal tears, and corners lost, all without loss, scattered small or light stains, occasional light browning, withal AN EXTRAORDINARILY FINE COPY. Eighteenth-century calf tooled in blind, the spine elaborately gilt, red edges; skilfully rehinged, upper joint split, hinge tender, rubbed, scraped, corners worn. Red levant solander case

FIRST FOLIO EDITION: "INCOMPARABLY THE MOST IMPORTANT WORK IN THE ENGLISH LANGUAGE" (Pforzheimer)

"Containing as it does the first editions of half of Shakespeare's plays (*The Tempest, Two Gentlemen of Verona, Measure for Measure, Comedy of Errors, As You Like It, Taming of the Shrew, All's Well, Twelfth Night, Winter's Tale, King John, 1 Henry VI, Henry VIII, Coriolanus, Timon of Athens, Julius Caesar, Macbeth, Anthony and Cleopatra,* and *Cymbeline*), the first good texts of four others (*Merry Wives, Henry V,* and *2* and *3 Henry VI*), and a different version of one play which had already appeared in a 'good' quarto (*Hamlet*), the volume from a literary point of view may well be considered the most important printed book ever issued." (Willoughby [vii])

The present copy is specially distinguished not only by its unusually fine condition, but further by the variant readings and other annotations, amounting altogether to more than two hundred words, written throughout the text of *Midsummer's Night Dream* and here and there in *King Lear*. These were the work of Charles Jennens, who owned this copy from about 1750 till his death in 1773, and whose editions of *King Lear* and four other Shakespeare plays were printed 1770-74

STC 22273; Greg III 1109-13; Pforzheimer 905; Bartlett 119; Pollard 108-41; E. E. Willoughby *The Printing of the First Folio* (1932), passim; Sir Sidney Lee *Shakespeares Comedies, Histories, & Tragedies...: A Census of Extant Copies* (1902), no. 22

continued

Mr. WILLIAM
SHAKESPEARES
COMEDIES,
HISTORIES, &
TRAGEDIES.

Publiſhed according to the True Originall Copies.

Martin Droeſhout ſculpſit London.

LONDON
Printed by Iſaac Iaggard, and Ed. Blount. 1623.

Provenance: (1) GL (initials or pressmark on pastedown); (2) Charles Jennens (1700-1773) of Gopsall, Leics., Shakespearean editor, friend of G. F. Handel, and author of the words for Handel's *Messiah* (1742), acquired by Jennens about 1750 possibly for £1/5/- (in pencil on free endpaper) (Lee), and bequeathed to his kinsman the: (3) Hon. Penn Assheton Curzon (*d.* 1797), eldest son of Assheton Curzon, 1st Viscount Curzon, and bequeathed presumably to his widow: (4) Sophia Charlotte Howe (1762-1835), Baroness Howe of Langar, daughter of the celebrated admiral and niece of the American revolutionary general, and bequeathed to their son: (5) Richard William Penn Howe (1796-1870), 1st Earl Howe, and passed through the succeeding earls to: (6) Richard George Penn Howe (1861-1929), 4th Earl Howe, sold by him in our London rooms, 21 December 1907, lot 37, £2035, to: (7) Francis Edwards, London, who by January 1910 had perfected leaf 2d3 and restored the first two leaves to their original condition, and later the property of: (8) John M. Robertson, Esq., of Largs, Argyllshire, sold by his heirs in our London rooms, 14 June 1965, lot 242 (part), £23,000, to: (9) John Fleming, New York, and thereafter the property of: (10) Paul Francis Webster

$300,000-400,000

□ 74   SHAKESPEARE, WILLIAM. Comedies, Histories and Tragedies... The second impression. *London, 1632 [i.e., ca. 1641]*

Folio (12¾ × 8⅝ in.; 322 × 220 mm.). Engraved portrait of Shakespeare by Martin Droeshout on title, woodcut capitals and ornaments; first sixteen leaves trivially wormed in the lower margins, A2-5 headrules barely shaved, four tiny rust-holes costing parts of a few letters, tiny natural paper fault in 2r5 costing a bit of the outer border-rules, four corners torn away without loss, small hole in V5 costing tiny fractions of three letters, 2l5 split without loss, some leaves lightly dampstained, scattered dust-soiling, small stains, and slight foxing. Eighteenth-century mottled calf tooled in blind and gilt; skilfully rebacked and recornered, original spine laid down, trifle rubbed. Crimson levant solander case.

SECOND FOLIO edition, third and rarest issue (Allot 3, Todd IIIb)

STC 22274e.5; Greg III 1116; W. B. Todd, in *Studies in Bibliography* V (1952), pp. 81-108

Provenance: (1) GB (initials on *1r); (2) Montagu Garrard Drake, Esq., of "Shardelois," Bucks., not before 1708 (bookplate on title verso); (3) Bernard Quaritch Ltd., London, 27 November 1923 (collation note on lower pastedown); (4) The Rosenbach Company, New York, before 1929 (cataloguing laid in); (5) Robert Walsingham Martin (1871-1961), of New Rochelle, N.Y. (bookplate), his sale in our rooms, 12 November 1963, lot 405, $2400; (6) Paul Francis Webster

$15,000-20,000

□ 75 SHAKESPEARE, WILLIAM. Comedies, Histories and Tragedies... The third impression. *London, [1663-]1664*

Folio (13 × 8½ in.; 329 × 214 mm.). Engraved portrait of Shakespeare by Martin Droeshout facing title, woodcut capitals and ornaments, the 1663 title (without portrait, as usual, and with the date altered in manuscript) inserted at the beginning (as often); Z6 supplied from a shorter copy, B1 badly torn but skilfully mended with only one letter lost, about six tiny rust-holes and about eleven small natural paper faults costing altogether about twenty letters, several short marginal tears some skilfully mended, few other trifling defects. Early nineteenth-century russia tooled in blind, all edges gilt; skilfully rebacked. Black morocco solander case

THIRD FOLIO edition, second issue, FIRST COMPLETE EDITION containing the first printing of *Pericles*

Wing S2914; Greg III 1118; Pforzheimer 909; Bartlett 122; Pollard 145-46

Provenance: (1) Herman Frasch Whiton (bookplate); (2) Paul Francis Webster

$20,000-25,000

□ 76 SHAKESPEARE, WILLIAM. Comedies, Histories and Tragedies... The fourth edition. *London: for H. Herringman, E. Brewster, and R. Bentley, 1685*

Folio (14¼ × 9⅛ in.; 360 × 232 mm.). Engraved portrait of Shakespeare by Martin Droeshout facing title, woodcut capitals and ornaments, several signatures in the Histories corrected or supplied in manuscript as often; first owner's signature on the blank recto of the portrait leaf showing through the portrait and eroded in one spot and neatly restored, affecting part of the portrait background, contents list numbered and the additional plays noted by an early hand, E6 folded in the press and so printed without loss, 2H1v lightly inked in the press near the outer margin and eighteen letters neatly darkened by an early hand, trifling marginal wormholes in G5-N1, about five tiny rust-holes and about eight natural paper faults affecting altogether about twenty-eight letters, two corners and a bit of one margin torn away without loss, a few very trifling tears, splits, smudges, and light stains, all without loss, withal AN EXTRAORDINARILY FINE COPY. Contemporary calf, red edges; skilfully rebacked to style with the original red-morocco lettering-piece laid down, sides somewhat rubbed and scraped

FOURTH FOLIO edition, FIRST ISSUE (without Chiswell in the imprint), FIRST SETTING of sheets 2B3.4 etc. (with the border-rules)

Wing S2915; Greg III 1119(*); Pforzheimer 910n; Bartlett 123; Pollard 146-47

Provenance: (1) William Legge (1672-1750), 1st Earl of Dartmouth (signed "W. Legge–1688" on the first recto, and "Dartmouthe" on title verso, engraved armorial bookplate); (2) Harry A. Levinson, Beverly Hills, 23 November 1962 (cataloguing laid in); (3) Paul Francis Webster

$7,000-11,000

M^r. William Shakefpear's
COMEDIES,
HISTORIES,
AND
TRAGEDIES.

Publifhed according to the true Original Copies.

Unto which is added, SEVEN

PLAYS,

Never before Printed in Folio:

VIZ.

Pericles Prince of *Tyre*.	Sir *John Oldcafle* Lord *Cobham*.
The *London Prodigal*.	The *Puritan Widow*.
The Hiftory of *Thomas* Lord	A *Yorkfhire* Tragedy.
Cromwel.	The Tragedy of *Locrine*.

The Fourth Edition.

LONDON,

Printed for *H. Herringman*, *E. Brewfter*, and *R. Bentley*, at the *Anchor* in the *New Exchange*, the *Crane* in St. *Pauls* Church-Yard, and in *Ruffel*-Street *Covent-Garden*. 1 6 8 5.

FRANKENSTEIN;

OR,

THE MODERN PROMETHEUS.

IN THREE VOLUMES.

Did I request thee, Maker, from my clay
To mould me man? Did I solicit thee
From darkness to promote me?——
PARADISE LOST.

VOL. I.

London:
PRINTED FOR
LACKINGTON, HUGHES, HARDING, MAVOR, & JONES,
FINSBURY SQUARE.

1818.

77

□ 77 [SHELLEY, MARY WOLLSTONECRAFT.] Frankenstein or the Modern
Prometheus. *London: Printed for Lackington, Hughes... 1818*

3 volumes, 12mo. Half-titles, publisher's advertisements (2 pp. -vol. I; 8 pp.
-vol. II; 4 pp. -vol. III); marginal stains and soiling, primarily in first
volume, tear along inner margin of I12 (vol. III). Original boards, uncut;
rebacked with red, rubbed. Red morocco folding box by Sangorski & Sutcliffe

First edition

Wise *Shelley* p. 8; Bleiler p. 178; Tinker 1881

Provenance: contemporary signature of H. Gott in Volume II

$5,000-7,000

☐ 78 SHELLEY, PERCY BYSSHE. Adonais. An Elegy on the Death of John Keats... *Cambridge: Printed by W. Metcalfe,... 1829*

8vo. Tear on pp. 1-2 and 15-16 repaired, text legible, waterstain of pp. 4-5 slightly affecting adjoining leaves. Blue morocco gilt by Riviere, green wrappers bound at back; upper cover detached

Second edition but first English edition the first edition being published in Pisa

Grannis pp. 72-3; Hayward 229; Grolier *English* 73; Ashley V 79; Wise, *Shelley* p. 61

Provenance: the Kern-Charles Auchincloss copy, sold at Anderson Galleries, January 21-24, 1929, lot 1096 and at Parke-Bernet, November 30, 1961, lot 506

$300-400

☐ 79 SHELLEY, PERCY BYSSHE. Hellas, A Lyrical Drama. *London: Charles and James Ollier, 1822*

8vo. Half-title. Green morocco gilt by Riviere; some fading

First edition

Granniss pp. 73-5; Wise *Shelley* pp. 66-7; Tinker 1903; Sterling 772

Provenance: the Charles Kalbfleisch copy with bookplate; also a bookplate with initials SSB

$400-600

☐ 80 SHELLEY, PERCY BYSSHE. Prometheus Unbound. A Lyrical Drama in Four Acts with other Poems. *London: C. and J. Ollier, 1820*

8vo. Half-title, portrait frontispiece; lacking leaf of advertisements, repair of inner margin of half-title, foxed. Blue morocco elaborately gilt with inlaid foliage and fruit, morocco doublures, inlaid dentelles; rubbed, upper cover detached, paper backing of silk free endpaper very creased

First edition

Granniss pp. 59-60; Hayward 228; Wise, *Shelley* pp. 55-6; Tinker 1898; Sterling 169

$300-500

☐ 81 [SHERIDAN, RICHARD B.] The School for Scandal. A Comedy as it is performed at the Theatre-Royal in Drury-Lane. *Dublin: Printed in the year 1782*

12mo. Uncut, with a leaf from the *American Negotiator* bound in at the back. Red morocco gilt by Birdsall

An early piracy

Provenance: the Templeton Crocker copy with his booklabel

$200-250

□ 82　SPENSER, EDMUND. The Faerie Queen... [Second Part.] *London: Printed [by John Wolfe] for William Ponsonbie, 1590; Printed [by Richard Field] for William Ponsonby, 1596*

2 volumes, sm.4to. Woodcut of St. George and the dragon, the Welsh words on p. 332 not filled in; margins trimmed, occasionally affecting signature marks or running headlines, careful restoration with a few letters supplied in facsimile on the last text page in the first volume, slight soiling or staining, washed. Uniformly bound in brown morocco gilt by Sangorski & Sutcliffe with a brown morocco solander case

First editions. First volume as originally issued without the additional gathering Qq of complimentary sonnets. With the dedication on the verso of the title and the first digit of the date on the title under the "r" in "for"

Pforzheimer 969,970; Grolier *English* 12; NSTC 23081,23082; Johnson 9,11

Provenance: the Herschel V. Jones-Hannah Rabinowitz copy. This was one of the Rabinowitz "lost" books; sent to Stockholm in 1961 for an exhibition and due to various complications misdirected and not located until August 1962 by which time the insurance company had become the owners. These volumes as well as the other "lost" books, including the Gribbel copy of "Alice" and the first English translation of Boccaccio's *Decameron* printed in 1620, were sold at Parke-Bernet, December 4, 1962. This was lot 203

$12,000-18,000

□ 83　[STERNE, *Rev.* LAURENCE.] A Sentimental Journey through France and Italy. By Mr. Yorick. *London: Printed for T. Becket and P.A. Dehondt, 1768*

2 volumes in one, 8vo. Half-titles, list of subscribers; M7 & 8 (vol. I), N7 & 8 (vol. II) torn along upper blank margin, title of second volume shorter at fore-edge, without the "advertisement" leaf which appears in some copies, slight soiling or browning. Contemporary calf; some chipping at head of spine, light rubbing, short crack along joints

First edition, with "vous" reading on p. 150, line 12 (vol. I) and "who have" on the last line p. 133 (vol. II). One of 135 copies on "fine" or imperial paper (printer's memorandum on manuscript in British Museum supplied edition size). This copy measures $6\frac{3}{8} \times 3\frac{15}{16}$ inches

Cross pp. 603-4; Rothschild 1971; Grolier *English* 54; Tinker 1978; Sterling 808

Provenance: bookplate of Sir John Throckmorton, Bart; inscribed by the British Prime Minister "Pauline Cotton from H.H. Asquith 8 July 1910"

$1,000-1,500

82

□ 84 STEVENSON, ROBERT LOUIS. Treasure Island. *London: Cassell and Company, 1883*

8vo. Half-title, 4 pp. publisher's advertisements dated 5G-783, frontispiece map; some spotting or foxing. Original green cloth: joints rubbed, cracking along inner hinges but firm. Green morocco-backed slipcase

First edition: without the "7" in the pagination of p. 127, "dead man's chest" is not capitalized on either p. 2 or 7, "worse" for "worst" on page 197 line 3, and lacking the period in line 20 on page 178. With the label of D. Wyllie & Son, Bookseller & Stationers and Circulating Library"

Beinecke 24

The lot includes a framed cabinet photograph of Stevenson with his signature in another hand

$1,000-1,500

85

☐ 85 STOWE, HARRIET BEECHER. Uncle Tom's Cabin, or Life among the Lowly. *Boston: J.P. Jewett, 1852*

2 volumes, 8vo. Title vignettes, 6 plates; title and final leaves of text foxed, faint intermittant foxing or spotting elsewhere. Original red "gift" binding with covers and spine stamped in gilt, all edges gilt; slight soiling, very careful repair to heads and tails of spines affecting the imprint at the foot of Vol. I, careful repairs along lower inner hinge of first volume, volumes skilfully recased. Brown morocco-backed slicase

First edition, with J.P. Jewett & Co at the foot of the spines and the Hobart and Robbins slug on the copyright page. "The passage of the Fugitive Slave Law in 1850 aroused a hatred against slavery which, except for the strident voices of the abolitionists, had been more mute than expressed. Mrs Stowe was one of those converted by the act's inhumanity... The result of her determination was her famous novel... when it appeared as a two-volume work, it quickly became a runaway sensation. The first week, 10,000 copies were sold; within the year the figure rose to 300,000. In the South she became a hated woman whose book, according to a literary journal, was 'a criminal prostitution of the high functions of the imagination.' To many more she was the little lady who caused the Civil War and freed the slaves." (*Negro History 1553-1903. An Exhibition of Books... of the Library Company of Philadelphia and the Historical Society of Pennsylvania...* Philadelphia, 1969, number 94)

Grolier *American* 61; PMM 332; Grolier *English* 91; Sabin 92457

Provenance: bookplate of Herbert Ten Broeck in each volume

$2,500-3,500

☐ 86 SUCKLING. *Sir* JOHN. Fragmenta Aurea. A Collection of all the Incomparable Peeces... *London: Printed [by Susan Islip and Ruth Raworth] for Humphrey Moseley, 1646*

8vo. Engraved portrait of Suckling by William Marshall, carefully restored, some offsetting or spotting, heaviest at front. Rose morocco gilt by Riviere; spine faded, light rubbing

First edition, with the first line of the title in large even capital letters and with the imprint "by T.W. for Humphrey Moseley" on the divisional title for *Aglaura*. A large copy measuring 7 × 4¼ inches

Pforzheimer 996; Grolier W-P 104; Hayward 84; Tinker 2000 (variant title)

Provenance: the Templeton Crocker copy with his booklabel

$400-600

☐ 87 [SWIFT, JONATHAN.] Travels into Several Remote Nations of the World. By Lemuel Gulliver... *London: Printed for Benj. Motte... 1726*

2 volumes, 8vo. Engraved portrait, four maps and two plans; marginal soiling and light browning. Contemporary calf; carefully rebacked and repaired

First edition. Teerink's "A" edition, with the portrait in the second state

Teerink 289; Rothschild 2104-6; Grolier *English* 42; PMM 185

Provenance: with the signature of T.R. Charlton on endpapers

$4,000-6,000

□ 88 SWINBURNE, ALGERNON C. Poems and Ballads. *London: John Camden Hotten, 1866*

8vo. Half-title, 8 pp. publisher's advertisements of Swinburne works tipped in before front free endpaper; faint soiling. Original green cloth, gilt lettered spine; some bubbling of cloth, lower inner hinge cracked, some rubbing. Red morocco solander case

PRESENTATION COPY inscribed on title-page "from A.C. Swinburne St. Clair. Baddeley. 1888". Above the inscription is the signature "B.W. Procter," the writer Barry Cornwall who died in 1874. He was a friend of Swinburne who presumably obtained the book after Procter's death

Second edition, with pp. 127 and 198 properly numbered, with "shaken" on p. 187, line 7, register marks in the lower center, without "Bradbury, Evans and Co." imprint at foot of p. 344

Tinker 2012; Hayward 280 (for Moxon imprint); Ashley VI 61

$250-400

□ 89 [SWINBURNE, ALGERNON C.] DICKENS, CHARLES. A Christmas Carol. In Prose. *London: Chapman and Hall, 1886*

8vo. Plates by John Leech. Original red cloth gilt; some soiling and rubbing, corner creased, inner hinges cracking, blindstamp of W.H. Smith and Son on endpaper

PRESENTATION COPY, inscribed by Swinburne to his very dear friend and companion, "Walter Theodore Watts from his affectionate friend A.C. Swinburne Christmas Day 1886."

$500-750

□ 90 THACKERAY, WILLIAM MAKEPEACE. Vanity Fair: Pen and Pencil Sketches of English Society. *London: Published at the Punch Office... 1847-48*

In the original 19/20 parts, 8vo. Illustrated, engraved title and 39 plates (without the original tissues), advertisements and slips as called for by Van Duzer and/or Randall; some foxing, a little soiling. Original printed wrappers; some repairs and light soiling, back wrappers to part VII supplied from a part III, back wrapper to XIII and XVII also supplied. Red morocco solander case

First edition with the heading on page 1 in rustic type, the woodcut of the Marquis of Steyne on p. 330 and the reading "Mr. Pitt" on p. 453 (as in entire first edition- see Randall p. 2). Part I, page 29 has 20 lines of text, parts XVII and XVIII have the wrapper undated, part XIX/XX has "Thos. Murray" in imprint, parts XIV, XV, XVII, XIX/XX without brackets after volume number on the upper wrapper and the last three parts do not have a bracket before the price. The printed title reads "With Illustrations on Steel and Wood by the Author", the verso of the title "London: Bradbury And Evans, Printer, Whitefriars" and the dedication leaf has the last line set in small type

Provenance: the W. K. Bixby copy with his bookplate, sold at Parke-Bernet, October 19, 1939, lot 394, to Charles S. Langstroth

$3,000-5,000

90

□ 91   THACKERAY, WILLIAM M. Vanity Fair. A Novel without a Hero. *London:
Bradbury and Evans, 1848*

8vo. Plates by Thackeray; some foxing and browning mostly of plates.
Original blue blind-stamped cloth; spine carefully repaired, spine faded,
shaken. Red morocco solander case

First edition in book form, second issue. PRESENTATION COPY INSCRIBED ON
FLY-LEAF ON THE DATE OF PUBLICATION IN BOOK FORM "With the grateful
regards of WM Thackeray. July 18, 1848."

Reputedly inscribed to Charlotte Brontë, before Thackeray was aware of her
name or sex, in thanks for the dedication of the second edition of *Jane Eyre*.
Tipped onto the front endpaper is a green printed slip advertising
Pendennis, taken from the final issue of the parts publication of *Vanity Fair*;
this slip bears the pencilled signature of A. B. Nicholls who married
Charlotte Brontë in 1854. The front free-endpaper bears Nicholls's name,
in another hand. Also inserted is an autograph letter signed by Clement
Shorter, 2 pages 8vo, London, 6 February 1918, to Sir William Robinson
Nicoll, stating that the copy of *Vanity Fair* was purchased by him in 1894
from Nicholls who had taken it to Ireland following his wife's death. The
inscription is reproduced in Shorter's book *Charlotte Brontë and Her Circle*

Provenance: the Clement Shorter-Jerome Kern- Barton Currie copy, sold at
Kern's sale, Anderson Galleries, 24 January 1929, lot 1343 and at Currie's sale,
May 8 1963, lot 400. *Sold as an association copy, not subject to return*

$3,000-4,000

□ 92 THACKERAY, WILLIAM MAKEPEACE. The Newcomes. Memoirs of a Most Respectable Family. Edited by Arthur Pendennis Esq. Illustrated by Richard Doyle. *London: Bradbury and Evans, 1853-5*

In the original 23/24 parts, 8vo. Engraved titles and 38 plates, (some foxing) slips and advertisements as called for in Van Duzer (excluding color variations), with these exceptions: only 5 lines on the first page of "The Respirator" advertisement in part I; part V is lacking 4 pp. advertisement at the front beginning "This day is published..."; advertisements at the back of part IX are: Slip "Price Fourpence... the Illustrated Chrystal, Palace Gazette;" 2 pp. advertisement Waterlow and Sons for the Patent Improved Autographic Press; part X without the slip "Price One Shilling; Itinerary of the Great Northern Railway." Original printed wrappers; lower wrapper of part V detached, some soiling, careful repair to spines, chipping. Brown morocco backed solander case

First edition in parts issue

Van Duzer 147

$200-300

□ 93 THACKERAY, WILLIAM MAKEPEACE. The Virginians. A Tale of the Last Century. *London: Bradbury & Evans, 1857-9*

In the original 24 parts, 8vo. Engraved title and 46 engravings by Thackeray, slips and advertisements as called for by Van Duzer with the exception of the 20 pp. of advertisements in part XXIV headed "Grace Aguilar's Works" and a few variations in colors in the advertisements; some foxing of plates. Original yellow printed wrappers; light soiling and rubbing, careful repair to spines. Blue morocco-backed solander cases; some rubbing

First edition in parts, the last of Thackeray's books that he illustrated himself. With the misprint "actresses" instead of "ancestresses" on p. 207 (part VII)

Van Duzer 232

$200-300

□ 94 [VOLTAIRE, FRANÇOIS MARIE AROUET DE.] Candide, ou l'Optimisme, traduit de l'allemand de Mr. le Docteur Ralph. *[Amsterdam, or London: Marc-Michel Rey?], 1759* [bound with] Candide, ou l'Optimisme... Seconde Partie. *[N. P.], 1761*

Two parts in one volume, 12mo, pp. 299, 1(blank), 32. A-M^{12}, N^6; A-E^{12}, F^6. Tiny marginal wormholes in second part, marginal tear in C12 (2nd part). Contemporary green vellum, red leather label; light rubbing. Green cloth folding box

Wade's 59^x "first edition" of the first part with the paragraph that is critical of the German poets and not included in any other 1759 edition commencing "Candide était affligé de ces discours..." on p. 242. This work has caused numerous articles and enquiries into the "true first edition". Voltaire attempted to conceal the publishing history of this work and the resulting controversies show how well he succeeded. The second work is spurious

PMM 204; Wade, The First Edition of Candide." *Princeton University Library Chronicle XX, 1959*, p. 63

Provenance: Lord Forbes' copy with bookplate

$1,000-1,500

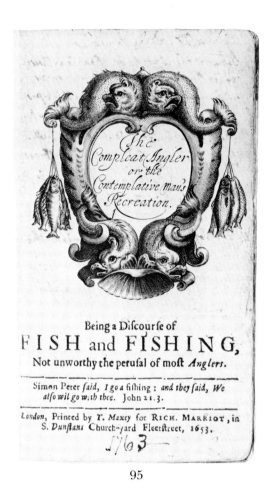

95

[WALTON, ISAAK.] The Compleat Angler or the Contemplative Man's Recreation: being a discourse of fish and fishing, not unworthy the perusal of most anglers. *London: by T. Maxey for Rich. Marriot, 1653*

Small 8vo. A large copy (5⅝ × 3⁹⁄₁₆ in.) with no cropping or shaving save a marginal comma on p. 245, engraved cartouche of dolphins and fish on title-page, 6 engravings of fish in text, that of the trout at the bottom of page with caption, 2 pages of words and music for "The Anglers Song" by Henry Lawes, the part for the bass voice printed upside down to allow two singers to face one another and share the book, with most of the 48 misprints and variations tabulated by Horne including "contention" for "contentment"; title-page slightly frayed at edges with some ink show-through from inscription on verso, a little mostly marginal staining and soiling throughout, 2 small wormholes at upper margin from L6 through Q4 affecting 2 text letters and several running heads, final 7 leaves supplied and restored, final blank (R4) lacking. Near-contemporary sheep; very rubbed, extensively restored

First edition. A very good copy of one of the most popular books ever published, a cornerstone of angling and English literature that has for more than 300 years delighted those who " love *quietnesse*, and *vertue*, and *Angling*"

Grolier *English* 31; Horne 1; Oliver 1; Pforzheimer 1048; Westwood & Satchell, p. 217; Wing W661

$5,000-8,000

96

☐ 96 [WESTMACOTT, CHARLES MALLOY.] The English Spy: An Original Work, Characteristic, Satirical, and Humorous. Comprising scenes and sketches in every rank of society. *London: Sherwood, Jones & Co. [vol. II Sherwood, Gilbert and Piper], 1825-26*

2 volumes, 8vo. 71 colored aquatints by Robert Cruikshank, Thomas Rowlandson and others, one plain plate, woodcuts in the text; some light browning of text. Blue morocco gilt, gilt dentelles, g.e., by Bumpus; dentelles and bookplates offset onto free endpapers

First edition. This anonymous satire on English high society was notorious in its day for its thinly disguised portraits of contemporary figures. Bound in at the end are two numbers (March and April 1826) of the *St James's Royal Magazine*, with six plates

Abbey, *Life* 325; Tooley 504

Provenance: Sir David Lionel Salomons, Bart of Broomhill, Tunbridge Wells, with bookplate; Gabriel Wells, sold at the sale of his stock at Parke-Bernet, November 13, 1951, lot 581

$1,000-1,500

☐ 97 WHITMAN, WALT. Leaves of Grass. *Brooklyn, 1855*

Folio. Portrait on heavy paper; creasing, some pages of preliminary matter loose, short tears along inner margin, pp. 90-94 coming loose (torn along inner margin). Original green cloth with title in gilt on both covers within gilt rules, gilt floral design, gilt edges, marbled endpapers; some staining and soiling, careful repairs. Green morocco-backed slipcase

First edition, without the Press notices

PMM 340; Wells & Goldsmith p. 4

$4,000-6,000

☐ 98   CHOQUE, PIERRE. *Le Combat de la Cordelière*. A Poem on a Sea Battle between the French and English Fleets in 1512, in French [*Brittany, c. 1514*]

ILLUMINATED MANUSCRIPT ON VELLUM (9×7¾in.; 229×197mm.), 23 leaves (first and last blank) plus contemporary vellum flyleaves pasted onto green silk, lacking one leaf after f.8 (perhaps an original cancel, see below) and f.5 should be bound before f.9, ff.2 and 5 cut out and trimmed and reinserted, else complete, collation: i² [i.e. blank plus frontispiece], ii⁴⁺¹ [the added leaf being the miniature transferred from before f.9], iii⁶ [of 8, one leaf cancelled and one miniature transferred to f.5], iv⁸, v², ruled in red, 20-22 lines, written in dark brown ink in a formal lettre bâtarde with pronounced roman forms, headings in red, small initials and paragraph marks in liquid gold on blue or orange-brown grounds, SEVENTEEN ILLUMINATED INITIALS (one- to 5-line) in delicate leafy and floral designs in grisaille on liquid gold grounds, TWO FULL-PAGE COATS-OF-ARMS (ff.2 and 8) and TWO FULL-PAGE MINIATURES within liquid gold frames, some wear and slight creasing, extremities of miniatures cropped or trimmed, slight marks and offsetting, minor marginal worming at ends, old red velvet over pasteboards, green silk endleaves, green silk marker, g.e., in a full red morocco case, title gilt

Provenance:(1) WRITTEN FOR ANNE OF BRITTANY (1477-1514, Queen of France, wife of Charles VIII and Louis XII) BUT LEFT UNFINISHED ON HER DEATH AND COMPLETED FOR HER DAUGHTER, CLAUDE DE FRANCE (1499-1524, Queen of France, heiress of Louis XII, betrothed at the age of 2 to the future Emperor Charles V but married at the age of 15 to François de Valois (later François I of France), Duchess of Brittany on the death of her mother in 1513, Queen of France on the death of her father in 1515)

The central text here was written out for Anne of Brittany and includes her coat-of-arms and a miniature of the author presenting the volume to her. On the verso of the coat-of-arms is part of a prose dedication to Anne herself. Anne of Brittany, however, died on 9 January 1513, before the presentation had taken place. The author must have been left in some embarrassment. He revised the manuscript, perhaps deliberately cancelling part of the dedication to Anne (the leaf missing after f.8), adding a lament of the Queen's death (f.3), adding a *Rondeau* to the end of the poem in praise of Anne saying that the flower has died but that her daughter has succeeded (f.7*b*), and supplying a new dedication to Claude de France explaining that it had been his intention to give the book to Anne of Brittany but her sudden death had prevented this and now he offered it to her daughter and successor (f.4). There seems to be no doubt that this is the dedication manuscript itself. Claude de France died at the age of only 25. She was not pretty ("bien petite et d'étrange corpulence", says one account of her) but nonetheless had seven children in her short sad life. The only other manuscripts certainly made for her seem to be two devotional books (C. Sterling, *The Master of Claude, Queen of France*, New York, 1975) and Anne de Graville's *Histoire de Palamon et Archita* (Quentin-Bauchart, *Les Femmes bibliophiles*, II, p. 384)

continued

(2) There is an almost contemporary erased inscription on f.1, legible by ultra-violet light "Claude du pres jadis ma maistresse"; this may allude to Claude de France herself who in the text is the flower of the Champ Royal, the royal meadow ("du pré"). There are obliterated inscriptions at the top of that page and hidden under the green silk on the flyleaf; both could be deciphered with patience. (3) Sir Thomas Phillipps (1792-1872), MS.4467, bought c.1830 from James Taylor of Great Surrey Street, London ("Taylor", in Phillipps' hand on flyleaf); Phillipps sale at Sotheby's, London, 29 November 1966, Lot 79

Text: On 10 August 1512 the English fleet under Sir Edward Howard came upon the French fleet outside Brest off the coast of Brittany. A dual developed between the English ship *Regent* and the great Breton warship the *Cordelière*, commanded by Hervé de Portzmoguer. The English sailors had already boarded the *Cordelière* when a French sailor set fire to its gunpowder magazine. The ship exploded and the *Regent* was destroyed in the resulting fire. Of the two ships' companies only about 80 men survived. This was regarded as a great triumph of heroism by the French against superior odds, and the event was described in a Latin poem by Germain Brice, Anne of Brittany's secretary, *Chordigerae Navis Conflagratio*, Paris, 1513, emphasising the appropriateness of Anne of Brittany's motto, 'Rather Death than dishonour' (*Potius mori quam foedari*)

The present French verse text of Brice's poem is by Pierre Choque, herald of Anne of Brittany, chronicler, sailor (he was in the Levant in 1501) and artist. He was also author of accounts of the funeral of Anne of Brittany and of the marriage of Anne de Foix to King Ladislas of Hungary. The poem opens here on f.9, "Nereides deesses de la mer/Ie vous supply que maidez a descrire/ La grant vouloir et magnanime a mer/De Herveus qui cest voulu instruire...". The text appears to be KNOWN IN ONLY ONE OTHER MANUSCRIPT, Paris, Bibliothèque Nationale ms.fr.1672, published by Auguste Jal, *Marie-la-Cordelière*, 1845. It is unneccessary to emphasise the rarity and importance of secular renaissance poetical manuscripts on nautical subjects

Around the long poem here are other short pieces:
1. A lament on the death of Anne of Brittany, 22 lines, beginning "Contre roy mort perverse et dangereuse", (f.3); APPARENTLY UNIQUE AND UNPUBLISHED; 2. A prose dedication to Claude de France, beginning "Selon raison et opinion suffisante" (f.4); 3. *Champ royal,* a 55-line poem on Anne of Brittany as the fairest flower in the field, with a 5-line *Envoy* and a 12-line *Rondeau* on Claude de France as Anne's successor, the main poem beginning "Se mon parler estoit tout rethorique" (f.6); APPARENTLY UNIQUE AND UNPUBLISHED; 4. Part of the prose dedication to Anne of Brittany (f.8*b*); 5. The Epitaph of Hervé de Portzmoguer, captain of the *Cordelière,* beginning "Nobles princes le nom hereuse garde" (f.20*b*); 6. *Champ Royal,* a 55-line poem on the wisdom of Anne of Brittany or Claude de France, with a 4-line *Envoy* and a 12-line *Rondeau composé par le dict translateur,* the main poem beginning "Theophrastus eloquent orateur" (f.21); APPARENTLY UNIQUE AND UNPUBLISHED

Illumination: The manuscript has four full-page illuminations (ff.2, 5 and 5*b*, and 8). Leaves 2 and 5 have at some time been taken out and trimmed to shape, and they were probably loose when the seventeenth- or eighteenth-century note was added on the flyleaf, "Je vous prie de ne point ignorer les petits morceaux". When they were put back, f.2 was reversed (there are

continued

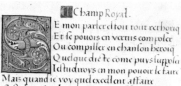

slight offsets from f.2 on f.3) and f.5 was moved from its original position facing f.9 (which also has tiny spots offset from f. 5*b*)

The illumination is provincial and idiosyncratic. Since the manuscript was made for presentation by the author himself and since Pierre Choque was a herald and artist by profession, the paintings may well be in the author's own hand. The style belongs to that of a group of curious commemorative manuscripts made in Brittany or Rouen for the funeral of Anne of Brittany (cf. esp. O. Pächt and D. Thoss, *Französische Schule*, II, Vienna, 1977, listing 17 such manuscripts on p.16) and the link with Pierre Choque, if upheld by further research, may clarify these manuscripts too

The miniatures are:

Folio 2. The arms of Claude de France, crowned, supported by an angel and a lion, surrounded by a gold cordelière, and with a dog and motto of the Dukes of Brittany "*A ma vie*" at the foot; landscape background

Folio 5. The author, kneeling in armour, presenting his book to Anne of Brittany who is enthroned and holding sword and sceptre; on her right are two allegorical figures, Justice (holding a sword) and a woman with a mirror and with books on her head (Wisdom?), and on her left are Temperance (holding spectacles and with a clock on her head) and a woman holding a tower and with a casket on her head (Fortitude perhaps?); the floor is tiled with the arms of France and Brittany, and the throne-room is richly hung with curtains including the Queen's motto "*Potius mori quam foedari*"; architectural border including three putti with a cordelière

Folio 5*b*. The battle on 10 August 1512 with the two ships alight and one man climbing the rigging of the French ship and other soldiers already in the water

Folio 8. The arms of Anne of Brittany, crowned and encircled with the cordelière, with the Queen's motto on a blue and gold scroll above

$10,000-15,000

☐ 99   BOOK OF HOURS, in Latin, with Calendar and some prayers in French.
[*Paris or Troyes, early fifteenth century*]

ILLUMINATED MANUSCRIPT ON VELLUM (6⅛×4⅛in.; 155×105mm.), 164 leaves plus 21 fifteenth-century added leaves (ff.167-187) and 4 original flyleaves, missing very many leaves and slightly misbound (ff.19-20 should precede ff.13-18, for example), gatherings mostly of 8ll., many with catchwords, 13 lines, written in dark brown ink in a gothic liturgical hand, rubrics in red, Calendar in blue, red and gold, capitals touched in yellow, versal initials and line-fillers throughout in burnished gold on blue and pink grounds with white tracery, 2- to 3-line initials in ivyleaf designs in blue, pink and orange on burnished gold grounds, APPROXIMATELY 140 THREE-QUARTER IVYLEAF BORDERS supported from a bar on the left-hand side of the text and including colored flowers and burnished gold ivyleaves with hairline stems, THREE LARGE MINIATURES WITH FULL BORDERS, the miniatures almost square and with 3-sided baguette borders supporting ivyleaf borders, prayers at end in several later hands, worn, two of the miniatures badly smudged (ff.56 and 91), other stains and smudges and signs of extensive use, nevertheless a sound manuscript and some pages fairly clean, modern red morocco, title gilt, g.e

Provenance: (1) The Use of the Office of the Virgin is that of Troyes but the manuscript belongs to a group of manuscripts probably made in Paris for use in Troyes and other towns in Champagne. (2) The name "Lougnonné" is roughly written in a cartouche on f.181, and a faint donation inscription upsidedown on the flyleaf reads "donné par charlotte doutreleaze" (probably sixteenth-century). (3) Ownership inscription of Maître Gervais George Lougnonné, sieur de Basmarse, 3 May 1707, on f.2

Text: The Hours of the Virgin is of the Use of Troyes, and the Calendar singles out in gold the patron saints of Troyes, SS.Mastidia (7 May) and Loup (29 July); St.Mastidia is also in the Litany (f.88). The texts are: Calendar, in French (f.3); Hours of the Cross (f.13, actually begins on f.19, misbound); Hours of the Holy Ghost (fragment only, f.21); Hours of the Virgin, Use of Troyes (f.22); the Penitential Psalms and Litany (f.72); the Office of the Dead (f.91); the *Quinze Joyes,* in French (f.156*b*); the *Sept Requêtes* (f.162*b*); and, as additions, the *O intemerata* (f.167); Memorials to the Saints (f.173); the Verses of St.Bernard (f.176); and further Memorials and prayers

Illumination: Though imperfect, this is a Book of Hours from an important workshop, that of the Troyes Master who was probably working in Paris from about 1390 to 1415. Features of the artist's style include his fine sense of space, pale harmonious colours, pale flesh colours, flecked skies, and serried hills surmounted by windmills. Fifteen related manuscripts from the workshop are recorded by M. Meiss, *The Limbourgs and their Contemporaries,* 1974, pp.406-7; of these, the one described there as in Hamburg was sold at Sotheby's in London, 11 July 1978, lot 50, and an unrecorded addition to the group was sold unrecognised at Christie's in London, 27 June 1979, lot 150.

continued

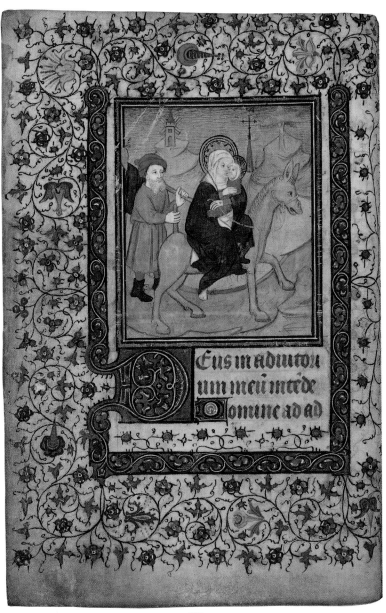

Eus in adintou
um meii inceôe
ônunc ad aô

99

The miniatures here are:
Folio 56. The Presentation in the Temple, the Virgin passing the Child to Simeon and attended by a maidservant with a candle and a basket of doves.
Folio 60*b*. The Flight into Egypt, Joseph following the donkey through a romantic landscape
Folio 91. A Funeral Service, with priests and mourners gathered around a bier

$2,500-3,500

☐ 100 THE POLIGNAC BOOK OF HOURS, in Latin, with Calendar in French [Paris, c. 1460-80]

ILLUMINATED MANUSCRIPT ON VELLUM ($6\frac{1}{2} \times 4\frac{1}{2}$in.; 163×114mm.), 228 leaves, plus 3 original flyleaves at beginning and 8 original added leaves at end, complete, gatherings mostly of 8 ll. (i¹², iv⁴, xv⁶, xxviii⁶) with a few traces of catchwords, 15 lines, written in dark brown ink in two sizes of a good gothic liturgical hand, rubrics in red, Calendar in red, blue and gold, capitals touched in yellow, versal initials and line-fillers throughout in burnished gold on red and blue grounds with white tracery, 2-line initials throughout in ivyleaf designs in red, blue and orange with white tracery on burnished gold grounds, PANEL BORDERS THROUGHOUT in the outer margin of every page in designs of colored flowers and acanthus leaves infilled with gold bezants, TWENTY-FOUR CALENDAR MINIATURES and THIRTY-ONE LARGE OR FULL-PAGE MINIATURES, five of them full-page with the text on a panel in the middle and the others in arched compartments with full borders of colored flowers and leaves and fruit (and sometimes birds) on liquid gold grounds and sometimes enclosing further small vignettes, coats-of-arms in several borders partly repainted (see below), large gold panels with mottos added on ff.25b and 159b, Cardinal's coat-of-arms added within an imitation medieval border on f.92b, prayers to Christ added in a sixteenth-century hand at end, extremities of full-page borders sometimes slightly cropped, some rubbing and flaking of miniatures (especially towards the beginning), all the arms slightly smudged, other wear and signs of use, generally sound and many miniatures quite fresh, old (perhaps even original) red velvet over wooden boards sewn on 5 thongs, joints and edges worn, spine repaired, some wear to nap but generally fine for velvet of such age, g.e., in a green quarter morocco fitted case, title gilt

Provenance: (1) Both the Hours of the Virgin and the Office of the Dead follow the Use of Rome, but the Calendar singles out in gold SS.Geneviève (3 January) and Denis (9 October), patron saints of Paris. (2) Seven of the miniatures include in the lower borders the coat-of-arms of a cardinal, barry of 6 *or* and *gules*, surmounted by a cardinal's hat. From the verso of these pages can be seen a similar shield, now overpainted, without the cardinal's hat. On f.92*b* the cardinal's arms occur added on a partially blank page. Clearly the manuscript was made for the man shown in the miniature on f.26, a layman in a black tunic, and later owned by a Cardinal of the same family. In 1949 the Cardinal was identified as François Guillaume de Castenau de Clermont-Lodève (d.1541), French ambassador to the Holy See and nephew of Cardinal d'Amboise. Though very close, however, his arms were not identical (A. Ciaconius, *Historiae Pontificum*, III, 1677, p. 251). The only Cardinal's arms which correspond precisely are those of MELCHIOR DE POLIGNAC (1661-1741), ambassador to Poland, plenipotentiary at the Congress of Utrecht, etc., son of Louis, vicomte de Polignac and marquis de Chalançon (M. Guarnaccius, *Historiae Pontificum*, II, 1751, cols. 247-250, and Anselme, *Histoire Généalogique*, IX, 1733, p. 300). The Cardinal died in Paris, but perhaps through him the book reached Italy in the eighteenth century when notes were added in Italian on the end flyleaves. (3) Captain R.G. Berkeley, Spetchley Park, Worcester; his sale at Sotheby's, London, 29 November 1949 ("Three Manuscripts of Exceptional Quality"), lot 19, described in capital letters as "UNQUESTIONABLY THE WORK OF MAÎTRE FRANÇOIS AND HIS PUPILS". (4) Apsley Cherry-Garrard, the Antarctic explorer; his sale at Sotheby's, London, 5 June 1961, lot 130, to Edwards

Text: The manuscript comprises: a Calendar, in French (f.1); the Gospel Sequences (f. 13); the *Obsecro te* (f.20*b*) and *O intemerata* (f.26); the Verses of St.Bernard (f.31); the Hours of the Virgin, Use of Rome (f.33); the Penitential Psalms and Litany (f.119); the Hours of the Cross (f.145); the Hours of the Holy Ghost (f.153); the Office of the Dead (f.160); and Memorials to the Saints (f.215)

Illumination: The first five large miniatures are in the style (and probably the actual hand) of one of the great illuminators of late fifteenth-century Paris, the so-called Chief Associate of Maître François. His name is unfortunate in that it implies that he was only some kind of assistant to Maître François, the famous artist recorded in 1473, but he evidently succeeded to the ownership of the workshop and his clients included the Duc de Bourbon, Charles VIII, Louis XII and Henry VII of England. Books of Hours by him include several in the Morgan Library in New York and the Psalter-Hours of Louis de Busco in the Walters Art Gallery (cf. J. Plummer, *The Last Flowering*, 1982, esp. pp. 68-9, with bibliography). The present manuscript was formerly ascribed to Maître François himself, and it shows the Associate closely following the work of the elder artist. The composition of the full-page miniatures here, spilling over into the borders, are typical of the best-known work of Maître François (cf. M. Manion, *The Wharncliffe Hours*, 1981, pls. 18, 26 and 27) and four of the Occupations of the Months in the Calendar are copied from the same patterns as those in the Wharncliffe Hours, but in reverse (February, March, May and September). The other full-page miniatures here are by a second artist, also working in the Parisian style established by Maître François

The subjects of the full-page and large miniatures are:
Folio 13. St. John on Patmos; swans, ducks and boats float past under a starry sky; below, the Evangelist is being boiled in a cauldron of oil before the Latin Gate while his executioners look on in irritation at their lack of success
Folio 15. St Luke in his study with books on the shelves, tables and lecterns and one open on his knee as he sits at his desk; the scene is set in an architectural frame which creates two levels: below, Luke as physician examining a specimen for a woman as two others wait their turns
Folio 17. St. Matthew in his study taking down his Gospel on a scroll at dictation from a kneeling angel; below, St. Matthew bringing back to life the son of King Hirtacus
Folio 19. St. Mark in his study seated at his desk and cutting a pen with which to write his Gospel; below, the martyrdom of St. Mark who is being dragged away on the instructions of a man in armour
Folio 20*b*. The angel appearing to Joachim as he tends his sheep in the countryside outside a city; the meeting of Joachim and St. Anne at the Golden Gate and the Annunciation; all set within an architectural framework
Folio 26. The Virgin and Child seated under a canopy and attended by a music-making angel, with the owner of the book kneeling before them
Folio 33. The Annunciation, Gabriel appearing to the Virgin in a gothic room and God the Father sending down the Holy Spirit from a high window; vignette scenes in the border show the Meeting at the Golden Gate, the Birth of the Virgin and the Presentation of the Virgin
Folio 46. The Visitation, in a landscape outside a town with a lake
Folio 60. The Nativity, Joseph and the Virgin adoring the Child with the ox and the ass in a crumbling stable

continued

eus in adiuto
rium meum
intende.
omine ad adiuuan

Folio 66. The Annunciation to the Shepherds, one of them kneels in wonder and their dog looks up at the angels who appear in the sky

Folio 71*b*. The Adoration of the Magi, who present their gifts to the Christ Child

Folio 77. The Presentation in the Temple with Simeon receiving the Child from the Virgin and her attendant handing over an offering to a priest

Folio 83. The Flight into Egypt, the Virgin feeding the Child on a donkey that Joseph leads past a falling classical statue

Folio 93. The Coronation of the Virgin, who is presented by two angels to God who is crowned with a triple crown

Folio 119. King David kneeling praying at an altar in a gothic tiled room; the border includes vignettes of David killing Goliath, David with Goliath's head being lauded by a group of girls playing music and David presenting Goliath's head to Saul

Folio 145. The Crucifixion, under a starry sky with the sun and moon, blood drips down the Cross from Christ's wounds and a figure in a Jewish hat turns to a group of soldiers with the words *"Vere Filius Dei erat iste"* (Matthew 27:54); the vignettes in the border show scenes from the Passion: Christ before Pilate, the Flagellation and the road to Calvary

Folio 153. Pentecost, in a crowded gothic room with the Virgin and St. John kneeling at a prie-dieu

Folio 160. A funeral-service outside a church porch, a priest reads the service as the sexton places the shrouded corpse in its grave

Folio 215. St. Michael, dressed in armour in a gothic interior open to the landscape beyond, overcoming Satan whom he tramples underfoot

Folio 216. SS. Peter and Paul, in a gothic tiled room

Folio 217. St. Nicholas restoring three children to life as they step out of a tub

Folio 218. St. Stephen being stoned by two soldiers in a landscape with a distant town

Folio 219. St. Sebastian, tied to a tree and shot full of arrows by three archers, one of whom wears parti-coloured hose

Folio 220. St. Lawrence, holding up his gridiron in a tiled interior

Folio 221. St. Christopher carrying the Christ Child across a choppy river

Folio 222. St. Mary Magdelene, holding a book and a pot of oil in a tiled room with a view of a distant town

Folio 223. St. Katharine, holding a sword and a book and with a broken wheel beside her, trampling an infidel king beneath her feet

Folio 224. St. Margaret in prison kneeling praying, as a dragon chews her cloak

Folio 225. St Anthony enthroned under a canopy, with his feet resting in a fire and a little pig watching him

Folio 226. St. Barbara, in a tiled interior, standing with one hand resting on her tower

Folio 227. St. Martha, holding a bucket over her arm and a dragon by a leash

The subjects of the Calendar miniatures are: a man feasting (f.1); a peasant pouring water into a river (f.1*b*); A man warming his feet (f.2); two fish (f.2*b*); peasants pruning vines (f.3); a ram (f.3*b*); a man carrying a tree through a spring landscape (f.4); a bull (f.4*b*); a young courtier and his lady hawking (f.5); a naked man and woman hiding behind a gold shield (f.5*b*); a man and woman raking (f.6); a crab (f.6*b*); a peasant making sheaves (f.7); a lion (f.7*b*); two peasants scything (f.8); a young girl holding a palm leaf (f.8*b*); a man treading grapes (f.9); a pair of scales (f.9*b*); a man sowing (f.10); a scorpion (f.10*b*); a man and pigs in a wood (f.11); a centaur (f.11*b*); a man slaughtering a pig (f.12) and a ram in a landscape (f.12*b*)

$25,000-35,000

BOOK OF HOURS, in Latin *[South West France, late fifteenth century]*

ILLUMINATED MANUSCRIPT ON VELLUM (6×3¾ in.; 153×95 mm.) 118 leaves (one blank), further blanks cancelled after ff.71 and 78, else complete, 6 additional leaves (4 on paper) and 10 additional leaves at end (on vellum), gatherings mostly of 8ll. (i-iv⁶), 21 lines, written in dark brown ink in a regular lettre bâtarde, rubrics in red, capitals touched in yellow, versal initials throughout in liquid gold on blue or dark red grounds, two-line initials throughout similar with partial borders with sprays of colored flowers and acanthus leaves, full-length borders throughout the Calendar, FIVE LARGE HISTORIATED INITIALS (7-line) in blue and dark red with leafy tracery in liquid gold, SIXTEEN LARGE MINIATURES in gently arched compartments within full borders of colored flowers and acanthus leaves on plain or liquid gold grounds and usually including grotesque monsters, many additions at ends (see below), some wear and rubbing, upper edges of full-page miniatures slightly cropped, LATE MEDIEVAL COLORED ENGRAVING added on last page (now partly torn away and very defective), early nineteenth-century English diced russia gilt, rebacked with spine laid on, marbled endleaves, g.e.

Provenance: (1) The Calendar suggests that the manuscript was intended for use in the Duchy of Auvergne, and the style of illumination links the book with the schools of Tours and Bourges a hundred or so miles to the north. (2) The additions at the ends are of considerable interest. Those at the beginning are dated 1515 (f.iv *b*) and those at the end show that the owner was a woman called Louisa ("pro me peccatrice" on f.119 and "me famulam tuam ludovicam" f.122). The prominence of St. Louis in red in the Calendar (25 August) may hint that the book was made for Louisa. The additions too include prayers against the Plague (f.126*b*) and to St. Roche (f.17, patron saint of sufferers from the Plague) and for the soul of a dying man (f.122*b*). The owner must have gone on a pilgrimage as there are a whole series of offsets from pilgrim badges on ff.v-vi. There are added prayers to the Three Kings whose shrine was in Cologne Cathedral (f.ii) and there is the remarkable engraving of the Mass of St Gregory on the last page, exactly the kind of ephemeral devotional image that pilgrims could buy in the Rhineland. Printed pictures like this very seldom survive in the actual manuscripts in which they were pasted. Proof that it is an original addition is supplied by the prayers to use with the engraving (f.122*b*) described here as granted by Pope Gregory who offered 14,000 years' indulgence to whomever says these prayers devoutly before this Image of Piety. The same offer of 14,000 years' indulgence occurs on a number of fifteenth-century prints of the Mass of St. Gregory (A. Shestack, *Fifteenth-Century Engravings of Northern Europe*, Washington, 1967, p. 212) and is said to derive from a sixth-century painting in Rome supposedly painted by St. Gregory the Great himself. (3) Sale at Sotheby's, London, July 10, 1967, lot 95

Text: The Hours of the Virgin are of the Use of Rome, but the Calendar singles out in red St. Martial of Limoges (30 June) and includes St. Ferreolus of Limoges (18 September) and no less than three obscure bishops of Clermont in Auvergne (SS. Bonitus, 15 January, Genesius, 3 June, and Gallus, 1 July) and SS. Clarus of Aquitaine (1 June) and Gerald of Aurillao (13 October), patron saint of upper Auvergne

The text comprises a Calendar (f.1), the Gospel Sequences (f. 13), the *Obsecro te* (f.17*b*) and *O intemerata* (f.20*b*), the Hours of the Virgin (f.25), the Hours of the Cross (f.72), the Hours of the Holy Ghost (f.75), the Penitential Psalms and Litany (f.79), the Office of the Dead (f.94) and Memorials to the Saints (f.116)

Illumination: The miniaturists of the Loire valley in the late fifteenth century adopted many of the stylistic innovations of Jean Fouquet including the hazy purple backgrounds and the clear separation of middle distance visible in the present manuscript. From Tours the style evidently filtered south to Bourges, where a group of related manuscripts can be ascribed to Jean Colombe and his workshop, and perhaps even further upstream. The present book may be from Bourges or Auvergne itself. Some of the compositions, such as Christ carrying the Cross and the figure of Death, derive from Tours Books of Hours like Vienna cod.s.n. 13247 and recur in Bourges manuscripts of Colombe. The iconography of Death riding an ox derives from Pierre Michault's poem La Danse aux Aveugles (cf. A. de Laborde, *La Mort Chevauchant un Bœuf*, Paris 1923) and recurs in another manuscript in the Tours style made for the south west of France (Sotheby's, London, December 10, 1973, lot 56). One great Bourges manuscript, the Moneypenny Breviary, includes the artist's name concealed in the lettering in one miniature; is there any significance in the apparent inscription in gold letters along the foot of the altar in the miniature on f.48*b*. "IO(?)EN DE MITISTER"? The miniatures here vary in quality. The finest, such as the picture of St. Mark (f.16), are excellent miniatures

The subjects of the large miniatures are:
Folio 13. St. Luke, seated at a desk in a classical interior, writing his Gospel as a bull watches him
Folio 14*b*. St. Matthew, taking dictation from an angel in magnificent gold renaissance armor
Folio 16. St. Mark, seen in profile sitting at his desk writing by an open window
Folio 17*b*. The Road to Calvary, Christ carrying the Cross attended by the Virgin and other holy women and pulled by a rope by a company of soldiers
Folio 25. The Annunciation, in a classical arcade looking out onto a river landscape
Folio 32*b*. The Visitation, St. Elizabeth wearing a turban, kneels and embraces the Virgin
Folio 40*b*. The Nativity; the Virgin, Joseph, the Ox and the Ass all kneel to adore the Child in the stable
Folio 43*b*. The Annunciation to the Shepherds, in a hilly landscape with their sheep and a goat and sleeping dog; the shepherds listen to one of their number playing the bagpipes as an angel appears overhead
Folio 46. The Adoration of the Magi, the kings with a great armed retinue present their gifts to the Virgin and Child
Folio 48*b*. The Presentation in the Temple, Simeon holds the Child at the altar as the Virgin kneels before them
Folio 51. The Flight into Egypt, Joseph leads the Virgin and Child on a donkey through a rocky landscape
Folio 55. The Assumption of the Virgin, the Virgin being raised through the landscape on a cloud of cherubim and crowned by four seraphim
Folio 72. The Crucifixion, the Cross surrounded by a regiment of soldiers, two of them in gold armor, while the Virgin swoons at its base

continued

101

Folio 75. Pentecost, in a classical interior, the Virgin enthroned with the apostles around her
Folio 79. King David and Bathsheba, David watches Bathsheba from outside his classical palace
Folio 94. Death seated on an ox pointing two arrows at a group of cowering soldiers and laymen on the edge of a wood where other skeletal figures hide among the trees

The subjects of the small miniatures are:
The Virgin (f.20); SS. Sebastian (f.116); Christopher (f.117); Anthony (f. 117*b*) and Michael (f.118)

$10,000-15,000

☐ 102   BOOK OF HOURS, in Latin, with Calendar and prayers in French *[Rouen, c.1520]*

ILLUMINATED MANUSCRIPT ON VELLUM (6½ × 3¾ in. ; 162 × 97 mm.), 145 leaves plus original preliminaries, complete, gatherings mostly of 8ll. throughout (i-ii⁶, xix⁴⁺¹), without signatures or catchwords, 20 lines, written in black ink in a small and very regular round roman hand in skilful imitation of printed type, rubrics in red, Calendar in black and red, one-line initials throughout in liquid gold on red and blue grounds with gold tracery, line-fillers throughout in liquid gold sometimes on red or blue grounds, 2-line initials throughout in grey with white tracery on liquid gold grounds, NINETEEN FULL ILLUMINATED BORDERS of scrolling acanthus leaves, flowers and birds on liquid gold grounds, TWENTY-ONE SMALL MINIATURES, one 2-line, one 3-line, three 6-line, thirteen 7-line, one 8-line and one 10-line, all of those larger than 3-line with full architectural borders in liquid gold, FOURTEEN LARGE MINIATURES with full architectural borders in liquid gold festooned with garlands and ribbons, extremities of some borders slightly cropped, small hole on f.115, generally in very fresh condition, with wide clean margins, SIXTEENTH- TO SEVENTEENTH-CENTURY RED MOROCCO, gilt frame, slightly worn, lacking clasp, edges gilt and gauffered, red quarter morocco case, title gilt

Provenance: (1) The liturgical use of the manuscript is for Rouen in northern France. Most of the manuscripts from this group are Use of Rome and the local use of the present manuscript may point to the area for which it was made

Text: The Calendar singles out the feasts of SS.Romanus (7th-century bishop of Rouen, 23 October and 17 June), Anne (26 July and 30 January), Sever (1 February), Ausbert (9 February), Austrebert (10 February), Hugh (9 April), Nigaise (11 October), and Mellon (22 October). All of these are local Rouenese saints. The Calendar also records the festival of the relics (3 December) of which the only other example is B.N.ms.lat.1407 and the feast of Notre-Dame des Neiges (5 August) which was not instituted in Rouen until 1454 by Guillaume d'Estouteville

The manuscript includes an unusual 4-line stanza in French for each month in the Calendar and the rest of the texts are: Calendar, in French (f.1), the Gospel and Passion Sequences (f.13), the *Obsecro te* and *O intemerata* (f.24b), a prayer to the Virgin (f.28), the Hours of the Virgin (f.29) of "mixed" type incorporating the Hours of the Cross and of the Holy Ghost, the Penitential Psalms and Litany (f.74b), the Office of the Dead (f.87) the Memorials to the Saints (f.116) the Verses of St.Bernard (f.123b), the *Stabat Mater* (f.125b), the Fifteen Joys of the Virgin (f.126b), prayers and verses to the Virgin and Christ for indulgences (f.127b), the *Ave Maria* (f.128) and the *Pater Noster* (f.139b) with a 14-line commentary in French on each phrase

continued

Omine labia mea aperies.
t os meum annunciabit lau

102

Illumination and script: This is a very pretty little manuscript closely related to the group designated by Myra Orth the 1520s Hours Workshop (Orth, "Progressive Tendencies in French MS.Illumination 1515-1530: Godefroy le Batave and the 1520s Hours Workshop", unpublished thesis, *N.Y.Inst.of Fine Arts,* 1976). Other examples include: Rosenwald Coll.no.10, Library of Congress; Doheny Coll. Camarillo; and Morgan M.452. Although the compositions in this manuscript do not repeat those of other manuscripts in the group as exactly as some of them copy each other, there are often very strong similarities. For example, the miniature of the Annunciation to the Shepherds (f.52) is very close to that in B.L.Add.MS.35318 f.47*b* and the Adoration of the Magi (f.56) to Morgan M.452 f.61. The miniatures of the present manuscript are painted in the classical renaissance style that Dr. Orth has defined as derived from the Antwerp Mannerists and Dürer and the widely disseminated prints of Marcantonio Raimondi. The closest

French antecedents are the works of the Master of Claude de France, whose delicate colors, classical genre and small scale are also thought to have derived from a northern, Italianate tradition. It has been convincingly argued that both the Master of Claude de France and the artists of the 1520s Hours workshop may have been Netherlandish craftsmen who moved to France (probably specifically to Tours) in the first decades of the sixteenth century (*The Last Flowering*, Pierpont Morgan Library, 1982). The flower and bird borders on liquid gold grounds in this manuscript are identical to those in B.L.Add.35318

Like the 1520s Hours workshop manuscripts and those by the Master of Claude de France, the present manuscript is written in the delicate roman script traditionally associated with Geoffrey Tory

continued

The subjects of the full-page miniatures are:

Folio 13. St.John on Patmos, his pen receiving divine inspiration from a vision of the Virgin and Child in the sky: full illuminated border on opposite page.

Folio 17. The Agony in the Garden, Christ praying before the chalice as the apostles sleep; a group of soldiers are arriving at the gate of the garden as dawn breaks; full illuminated page opposite

Folio 29. The Annunciation, in a classical interior the Virgin turns from her prie-dieu at the arrival of Gabriel and the Holy Spirit; full illuminated page opposite

Folio 36*b*. The Visitation, in a landscape where the Virgin is attended by three angels and St.Elizabeth by two women in contemporary sixteenth-century dress; full illuminated border opposite

Folio 44. The Crucifixion, set in a fine landscape with little groups of figures standing, running and on horseback in the distance; full illuminated border opposite

Folio 45*b*. Pentecost, set in a classical interior with the Virgin and apostles kneeling; full illuminated border opposite

Folio 47. The Nativity, in a tiled classical courtyard; full illuminated border opposite

Folio 52. The Annunciation to the Shepherds, in a fine landscape where one of them has fallen back in amazement and has to be supported by a shepherdess; full illuminated border opposite

Folio 56. The Adoration of the Magi, among classical ruins the three kings present their gifts while Joseph peers nervously out from a doorway; full illuminated border opposite

Folio 60. The Presentation in the Temple, Simeon holds the Child as the Virgin kneels and attendants with offerings watch; full illuminated border opposite

Folio 64. The Flight into Egypt, the Holy Family resting on the way as Herod's soldiers search for them in the background; full illuminated border opposite

Folio 69*b*. The Coronation of the Virgin, in a classical interior the Virgin kneels to receive her crown from God the Father; full illuminated border opposite

Folio 74*b*. King David, kneeling uncrowned in a classical courtyard as the angel of vengeance appears brandishing a sword above him; full illuminated border opposite

Folio 87*b*. The Raising of Lazarus, outside a church Christ raises his hand in blessing and the shroud and ropes fall from Lazarus; full illuminated border opposite

The subjects of the small miniatures are:

St.Luke (f.14*b*); St.Matthew (f.15); St.Mark (f.16); the Virgin and Child (f.26*b*); the Trinity (f.116); St.Michael (f.117*b*); St.John the Baptist (f.118); St.John the Evangelist (f.118*b*); SS.Peter and Paul, St.James (f.119); St.Stephen (f.119*b*); St.Sebastian (f.120); St.Nicholas (f.120*b*); St.Anne (f.121); St.Mary Magdalene (f.121*b*); St.Catherine; St.Margaret (f.122); St.Barbara (f.122*b*); St.Apollonia (f.123) and the Annunciation (f.128)

$15,000-20,000

103

□ 103 BOOK OF HOURS, in Latin. *[Flanders, perhaps Ghent early sixteenth century]*

ILLUMINATED MANUSCRIPT ON VELLUM (4¾×3½ in. 117×85 mm.), 235 leaves, lacking 2 text ll. after f.233 and a blank at end, perhaps lacking a Calendar, else complete, f.1 (frontispiece) perhaps originally bound before f.136, gatherings mostly of 8ll. with full-page miniatures on added sheets (xviii ¹⁺⁶), 15 lines, written in dark brown ink in a very good lettre bâtarde, rubrics in red, capitals touched in yellow, one and 2-line initials throughout in leafy designs in grey and white on red-brown grounds with white tracery, 2 bifolia (ff.168-171) by a second artist, TWENTY SMALL MINIATURES or historiated initials (one 4-line, seven 5-line, twelve 6-line), fifteen of them with three-quarter borders and five with full borders in the Ghent/Bruges style of naturalistic flowers and fruit scattered a yellow-gold or particolored ground and including realistic birds, insects, snails, etc., SEVEN FULL-PAGE MINIATURES in gently arched compartments with full borders in similar style, slight rubbing and wear, extreme upper edges of some full borders very slightly cropped, eighteenth-century red morocco gilt, edges gilt and painted with floral design, brown morocco fitted case, title gilt

continued

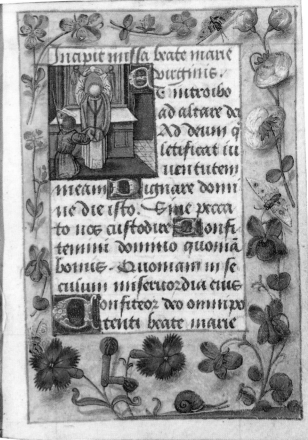

103

Provenance: (1) There is no Calendar but the Litany includes many Flemish saints (SS. Omer, Bertin, Amand, etc.) and St. Bavo, patron saint of Ghent, but not St. Donatian of Bruges. (2) Sale at Parke-Bernet, March 7, 1967, lot 122, illustrated as frontispiece

Text: Hours of the Cross (f.3); Hours of the Holy Ghost (f.13); the Mass of the Virgin (f.22); the Gospel Sequences (f.30); the Hours of the Virgin, Use of Rome (f.39); the *Salve virgo* in rhyming verse (f.136); prayers for use at Mass, preceded by an offer of 2000 years' indulgence said to have been sent by Boniface VI [pope for one year in 896] to Philip [king of France 1180-1223] (f.145*b*); the Penitential Psalms and Litany (f.150); and the Office of the Dead (f.179)

Illumination: This is a pretty Flemish Book of Hours with full-page miniatures on separate sheets in the syle which derives ultimately from the Master of Mary of Burgundy. The full-page miniatures are:

Folio 1b. Christ holding the orb and blessing (for similar miniatures, cf. P.M. de Winter in *Bull. Cleveland Mus. of Art,* LXVII, 1981, figs. 18-20); border on a red ground including violets and three birds

Folio 2b. The Crucifixion with the Virgin, St. John and Mary Magdalene on the left, and soldiers on the right; landscape background with view of a big church; border includes flies, a peacock and a caterpillar

Folio 12b. Pentecost, set in a gothic church with the Apostles around the Virgin; border includes two butterflies, a fly and a snail

Folio 21b. The Virgin and Child in the crescent moon, with two angels with symbols of the Passion; border includes a flowerpot with carnations, insects and a bird

Folio 38b. The Annunciation, set in a gothic building with Gabriel approaching the Virgin who kneels at a prie-dieu at the foot of her bed

Folio 149b. The Last Judgement, a splendid scene with Christ and all the saints in Heaven at the top left and the sky parting to show a landscape with a gothic church and village by a river, and an angel with a golden sword and lance herding a group of naked souls into the pit of Hell, border on a gray ground including birds scavenging among acanthus leaves

Folio 178b. A Death scene, set in a medieval domestic interior by a red-draped bed; the body is laid out on a mat beside candles and washing utensils as a man and two women sit watching; above, an angel and a devil fight for the soul of the dead man; border includes many bones and skulls wearing a papal tiara, a mitre, the imperial crown, a cardinal's hat, and a royal crown

The smaller miniatures are: the Descent from the Cross (f.3), the Ascension (f.13), the Mass of St. Gregory (f.22), St. John on Patmos (f.30), St. Luke painting (f.32), St. Matthew (f.34), St. Mark (f.36), the Visitation (f.39), the Meeting at the Golden Gate (f.62), the Nativity (f.77), the Annunciation to the Shepherds (f.84), the Adoration of the Magi (f.91), the Presentation in the Temple (f.97), the Massacre of the Innocents (f.103), the Flight into Egypt (f.113), the Coronation of the Virgin (f.122), the Virgin and Child and an angel with the Cross and nails (f.136), a monstrance with the Host (f.145b), David in prayer beside his palace (f.150) and two skeletons attacking three well-dressed noblemen riding through a landscape (f.179)

$12,000-18,000

☐ 104 BOOK OF HOURS, in Latin, with calendar in French. *[South West France, 1549]*

ILLUMINATED MANUSCRIPT ON VELLUM (7¼×4⅞ in.; 185×123 mm.), 156 leaves plus 2 original preliminaries, lacking single ll. after ff.50, 58, 80, 87, 94, 104, 108, 115, 121 and 3 blanks at end, else complete, gatherings originally of 8 ll. throughout with catchwords (within decorative cartouches on ff.57*b*, 64*b*, 72*b* and 115*b*, and within a face on f.87*b* and sketch map of a church around the word "iherusalem", perhaps the Church of the Holy Sepulchre, on f.101*b*), 16 lines, written in dark brown ink in a gothic liturgical hand, rubrics in red, versal initials throughout in liquid gold on red or blue grounds, 2-line initials in red, blue and orange with white tracery, SIX SMALL MINIATURES (five 5-line and one 4-line) in colors and liquid gold, SEVEN HALF-PAGE MINIATURES within full liquid gold frames and FULL-PAGE FRONTISPIECE within ornamental frame, a few early additions, some wear and signs of use, a few small spots of retouching to the frontispiece, some slight marks and dampstains, generally sound, MID SIXTEENTH-CENTURY FRENCH OLIVE-BROWN MOROCCO GILT, panelled with gilt ruling and fleur-de-lys corner stamps, central oval plaques of the Crucifixion, spine with over-all pattern of interlinked compartments *à la fanfare* with leafy and floral stamps, repaired, corners and spine skillfully restored, g.e., dark red morocco slipcase

Provenance: (1) The manuscript opens with a remarkable 18-line rhyming verse in French headed "Prosopopee" and signed "P.G.M.F." in which the book asks if you want to know who it belongs to ("Veulx tu sacavoyr a qui ie suis..."); it is owned by CHARLOTTE BOUTON, the glory of Angoumois ("l'honneur d'Engoulmoys") who, in the month of August 1540, had me made – says the book – by night and day, to pay a holy rent to Christ, her dearest love, and that the reader should pray for her and her husband, Chormelet, Sieur de Brisebarre, that they might one day live in Heaven. The name Charlotte Bouton is erased on the second flyleaf. The frontispiece, which is not by the same artist as the other miniatures, has a coat-of-arms *azure* a chevron *or* between 3 roses of the same. (2) Sale at Sotheby's, London, July 11, 1966, lot 240

Text: This is an exceptionally late Book of Hours, valuable for its precise date and rare localisation in south-west France. The Use is the very unusual version of Poitiers (Prime antiphon *O amirabile* and capitulum *Virgo verbo*, and None antiphon *Ecce maria* and capitulum *Et radicavi*), and the Calender singles out in red St. Ausonius, first bishop of Angouleme (22 May) and includes both feasts of St. Eparchius of Angouleme (14 March and 1 July). It also includes SS.Leger (nephew of a bishop of Poitiers, 2 October), Caprasius of Agen (20 October), St. Martial of Limoges (16 June, with his translation twice on 10 October and 12 November) and St. Pandulph from the diocese of Limoges (6 October). Angouleme itself is in Aquitaine about equidistant south of Poitiers and west of Limoges

The texts are: Calendar, in French (f.3), the *Obsecro te* (f.15), the Gospel Sequences (f.19), prayers on the Conception of the Virgin (f.24*b*), the Passion Sequence (f.27), the Hours of the Virgin (f.36) of "mixed" type incorporating the Hours of the Cross and of the Holy Ghost, the *Stabat mater* (f.93), the Penitential Psalms and Litany (f.95), and the Office of the Dead ending with a series of prayers to Christ with an offer of 20,020 years and 23 days' indulgence for their use, said to have been granted by Pope Calixtus III in 1456 as in book I of the papal register, f.213 (f.158)

104

Illumination: The rather naive provincial miniatures are interesting for their fixed date and strong influence from contemporary colored woodcuts from which derive the heavy black outlines and hatched shading. The large miniatures are:

Folio 2b (frontispiece). St. Peter, with keys and book
Folio 15. The Virgin and Child
Folio 27. Christ in the Garden of Gethsemane
Folio 59b. Pentecost
Folio 60b. The Nativity of Christ
Folio 66b. The Annunciation to the Shepherds
Folio 71b. The Adoration of the Magi
Folio 76B. The Presentation in the Temple

The smaller miniatures are: SS.John (f.19), Luke (f.20*b*), Matthew (f.22), Mark (f.23*b*), the Meeting at the Golden Gate (f.24*b*) and the Pieta (f.93)

$4,000-6,000

☐ 105 [PRESIDENTS OF THE UNITED STATES.] A handsomely bound 4to volume of portraits and documents representing America's first through thirty-second Presidents, most of the items being documents signed by the Chief Executives as President, each hinged on a page opposite a page carrying a tinted engraved portrait of the leader in question.

Crushed red morocco binding BY BAYNTUN, front cover with a gilt French fillet border, stylized foliate cornerpieces of alternating light and dark green morocco onlays, and a centered design of TWO FINE COSWAY-STYLE MINIATURES ON IVORY depicting George Washington and Franklin D. Roosevelt, the first and the last Presidents represented in this volume, within an elaborate foliate frame of green morocco onlay leaves and blue morocco onlay flowers heightened with gilt and set with numerous rhinestones, rear cover with a gilt French fillet border, spine gilt in six compartments, gilt-lettered in two, the remaining four with cornerpieces of green morocco onlays after the manner of the front cover, watered green silk doublures with crushed red morocco border gilt, watered green silk linings, all edges gilt; with a red buckram box. The manuscripts in the series consist of:

WASHINGTON, GEORGE. Printed Document signed ("Go: Washington") as President, accomplished in another hand, one page folio completely separated at its center fold and mounted as two pieces on separate leaves of the volume, Philadelphia, [ante 14 December 1793], being three-language ship's papers for the brig *Lydia* of Salem, Mass., Ebenezer Shillaber, master, countersigned by Secretary of State Thomas Jefferson; browned, foxed; the portion of the folio leaf carrying Washington's signature and the paper seal rebacked, this leaf with extensive paper looses at separating folds and with damage to the seal; giving Shillaber leave to take his ship and her load of "Flour, and Corn, and Two hogsheads of Lampblack" from Baltimore to the island of Madeira

ADAMS, JOHN. Signature as President on an 8vo oblong, being the lower portion of a Printed Document on vellum, [ante 29 August 1797], countersigned by Secretary of State Pickering; paper seal intact, cancellation slit through Adam's signature, soiled on verso

JEFFERSON, THOMAS. Printed Document signed as President ("Th: Jefferson"), accomplished in another hand, Philadelphia, [ante 23 May 1804], being four-language ship's papers for the ship *Endeavour* out of Salem, James Buffenton master, countersigned by Secretary of State James Madison; paper seals intact, skilful repairs on verso to paper loses at separating folds (one affecting a character of Jefferson's signature), one unrepaired splitting fold; being the passport for the *Endeavour's* voyage to Copenhagen with a cargo of logwood, sugar, coffee, and nankeens

MADISON, JAMES. Printed Check accomplished and signed as President, an oblong 7 ⅞ inches × 2 /34 inches, Washington, 25 October 1813, being a printed check on the Office of Pay and Deposit of the Bank of Columbia, to the order of "A.B. or bearer"for $150; browned, some spotting, with cancellation slits

MONROE, JAMES. Signature ("Jas Monroe") as Secretary of State, on a small oblong cropped from a printed document

ADAMS, JOHN QUINCY. Printed Document signed ("J.Q. Adams") as President, 1 page folio oblong on vellum, Washington, 5 October 1826, being a land grant to Samuel Scott of Morgan County, Indiana; wax seal removed, soiled, accomplishment faded, but Adam's signature clear

continued

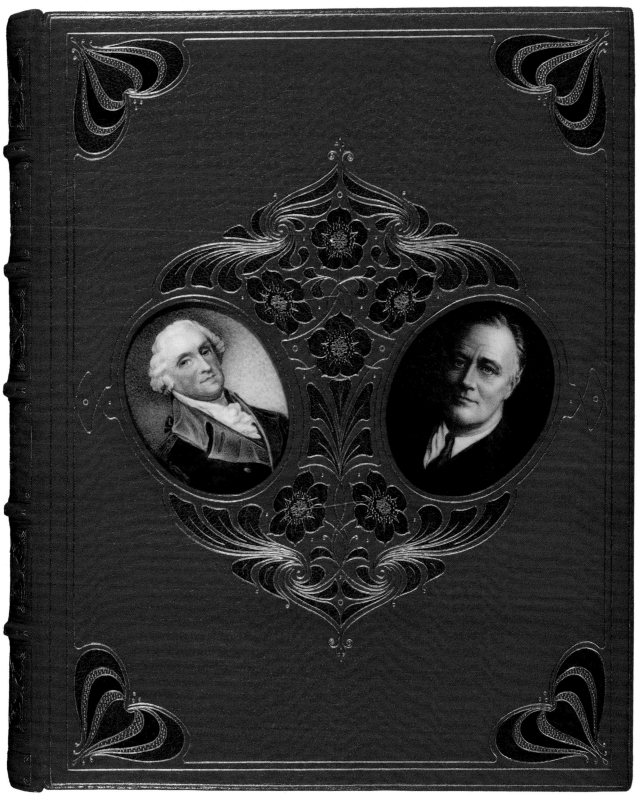

JACKSON, ANDREW. Signature as President, being a small oblong cropped from a printed Document, 1831

VAN BUREN, MARTIN. Printed Document accomplished and signed by a secretary, 1 page folio oblong on vellum, Washington, 1 November 1839, being a land grant to James Tillerton of Sangamon County, Illinois; paper seal intact, soil on verso, ink faded

HARRISON, WILLIAM HENRY. Autograph Document signed ("Wm H. Harrison"), 1 page 8vo, Greeneville, 20 June [ca. 1795], directing the commissary to "...issue for the use of the Putawatimie Indians four gallons of whiskey"; ink blots on recto and verso

TYLER, JOHN. Autograph Note signed, 1 page small 8vo, Sherwood Forest, Va., 2 November 1858, to Miss Jane Erasmus; sending "...my autograph... in pursuance of her polite request..."

POLK, JAMES K. Signature as President, small oblong cropped from a printed document, Washington, 24 July 1847

TAYLOR, ZACHARY. Signature ("Z. Taylor Bt. Genl, U.S. Army"), on a small oblong cropped from a Letter signed, n.d.

FILLMORE, MILLARD. Printed Document signed as President, 1 page folio oblong, Washington, [ante 21 June 1852], being four-language ship's papers for the whaling ship *China* of New Bedford, Willis Howes, master, countersigned by Secretary of State Daniel Webster; paper seals intact, splitting at folds; the *China's* papers for a voyage to the Pacific

PIERCE, FRANKLIN. Printed Document signed as President, 1 page 4to, Washington, 19 June 1854, being Pierce's authorization to affix the seal to a letter addressed to King Victor Emmanuel II; with integral blank, endorsed on verso, spotted and stained

BUCHANAN, JAMES. Printed Letter signed as Secretary of State, accomplished by a secretary, 1 page 4 to, Washington, 22 April 1845, to the Governor of Tennessee; neat taped repairs to folds of letter and its integral blank, soil at margins; being a form letter for the transmittal of federal sessions laws

LINCOLN, ABRAHAM. Printed Document signed as President, accomplished in another hand, Washington, 18 June 1864, being John K. Loring's commission as captain and Commissary of Subsistence, countersigned by Secretary of War Stanton; with decorative engraved vignettes at the head and foot of the commission, paper seal intact, soiled, mounting remnants on verso, fading of accomplishment

JOHNSON, ANDREW. Printed Document signed with a signature stamp, 1 page folio oblong, Washington, 24 July 1867, being Stanislaus Remak's commission as a second lieutenant, countersigned by Secretary of War Stanton; paper seal intact, margins browned and soiled, some fading of accomplishment

GRANT, ULYSSES S. Autograph Letter signed ("U.S. Grant"), 1 ¼ pages 8vo, Long Branch, N.J., 11 August 1882, to William Chatfield; with mounting remnant on verso of second leaf; responding to Chatfield's invitation: "...let me thank you now for your kind invitation and to express the regret that I can not accept for this summer."

HAYES, RUTHERFORD B. Autograph Letter signed, 1 page 8vo, Fremont, Ohio, 29 June 1891, to Benjamin Austin; mounting remnants on verso; complying to Austin's request for "...a portrait of Mrs Hayes—the favorite one—; [and] a letter of Vice President Wheeler..."

GARFIELD, JAMES A. Signature ("J.A. Garfield MC"), on a small oblong apparently cropped from a larger leaf

ARTHUR, CHESTER A. Signature as President, on a card with the printed legend "Executive Mansion, Washington"; slightly soiled, mounting remnants on verso

CLEVELAND, GROVER. Signature as President, March 1, 1 March 1897, on a card with the printed legend "Executive Mansion Washington"

HARRISON, BENJAMIN. Typed Letter signed ("Benj Harrison") as President, 1 page 8vo, Cape May Point, N.J., 1 September 1891, to Gen. Edward M. McCook in Riverside, Conn.; some soil at folds of integral blank; replying to McCook's letter concerning a recent military reunion, the President says that he is "…gratified to know that the few words I was permitted to speak to my comrades at Whitehall pleased and cheered them…"

McKINLEY, WILLIAM. Signature as President, on a card bearing the printed legend "Executive Mansion, Washington"

ROOSEVELT, THEODORE. Printed Document signed as Governor of New York, accomplished in another hand, 1 page folio, Albany, 25 May 1900, being a letter of recommendation for Henry J. Coggeshall, former state senator from Oneida County "to whom this may come"; with paper seal and ribbons intact

TAFT, WILLIAM H. Typed Letter signed ("Wm H Taft") as President, 1 page small 4 to, Washington, 24 June 1909, to A.A. Lawrence in Boston; with integral blank, soiled at margins; writing concerning his plans to be Lawrence's neighbor in Beverly, Mass., for the summer: "…It is very good of you to suggest rendering assistance in our entry of the house, but our arrangements are quite complete and I do not think there will be any difficulty in our moving in promptly Sunday morning, the 4th of July… It delights me also to hear that Bishop Lawrence is to receive a degree at Yale. I hope to be there on Commencement Day when it is conferred."

WILSON, WOODROW. Typed Letter signed as President, 1 page 4to, Washington, 6 December 1916, thanking Richard H. Gaines of New York for his "…kind letter of congratulation…"; with integral blank

HARDING, WARREN G. Signature, on a small oblong cropped from a Typed Letter signed, n.d., n.p.

COOLIDGE, CALVIN. Typed Letter signed as President, 1 page 4to, Washington, 15 October 1924, to Rae D. Henkle, editor of the *Christian Herald* in New York; some soil on letter and on its integral blank; congratulating Henkle on his paper's drive "…to impress upon its readers the necessity of voting at the coming election. The fact that the franchise is a duty as well as a privilege has been stressed again and again, but we are prone to forget that it is a privilege which has come to us, not as a natural right, but as the result of long years of struggle and suffering. Its neglect does not free that individual from responsibility, because this Government is what the people make it, and those who fail to take their part must hold themselves equally responsible for the ultimate result."

HOOVER, HERBERT. Typed Letter signed as President-elect, 1 page 4to, Stanford University, 18 November 1928, to Robley D. Stevens of the Philadelphia *Endeavour*; soiled; replying to a letter from Stevens and asking him to "…convey to your associates my appreciation for the friendship and good wishes which it [the letter] conveys to me…"

ROOSEVELT, FRANKLIN D. Typed Letter signed as Governor of New York, 1 page 4to, Albany, 21 July 1932, to Joseph H. Dryer, president of the National Council of Traveling Salesmen's Associations in New York; small tear in upper left margin; replying to Dryer's "awfully nice letter," Roosevelt declines an invitation to join the traveling salesmen on 30 August

$7,500-11,000

□ 106 [PRESIDENTS OF THE UNITED STATES.] ☆ ADAMS, JOHN QUINCY. Letter signed ("J. Q. Adams"), 1 page 4to, Washington, 23 April 1847, to Jonathan Wild in Braintree, Mass.; scattered spotting; acknowledging receipt of Wild's letter and concerning a pension claim ☆ PIERCE, FRANKLIN. Autograph Letter signed, 1 page 4to, Concord, N. H., 17 October 1849, to Lewis W. Alcock in Hancock, N. H.; concerning a legal matter: "... Your father should hold no conversation either as to a settlement or reference–Much talk about a trial here & in relation to your father. Robb &c is all perfectly idle or as your Mother properly calls his extravagant & wild statements *fabulous*..." ☆ ARTHUR, CHESTER A. Letter signed ("C. A. Arthur"), 1½ pages 8vo, New York, 11 October 1876, "Confidential" to Isaac Baker in Comstock, N. Y.; soil on verso of second leaf, ink smear in direction to Baker; responding to Baker's letter of 5 October: "... I at once took occasion to see the person who was mainly responsible for what formerly took place, and was assured by him that, so far as he was concerned, there would be no recurrence of it during your present canvass..."

Together 3 items

$275-325

□ 107 [PRESIDENTS.] ☆ POLK, JAMES K. Autograph Endorsement signed ("J. K. P.") as President, 6 lines, n.p., 14 June 1847, on the front of a blank envelope; lightly browned, soiled; writing: "Respond to the Secretary of the Treasury, whose attention is called to this application" ☆ CLEVELAND, GROVER. Autograph Letter signed as President-Elect, 1¼ pages 8vo, Albany, 17 December 1884, to Henry A. Ward; sending a check (not present) "... for mounting the deer head..." ☆ McKINLEY, WILLIAM. Autograph Letter signed ("Wm McKinley"), 1 page 8vo, Canton, Ohio, 1 October 1882, to Secretary of War Robert Lincoln; with endorsements on verso; writing to nominate W. T. Hughes for a clerkship in place of "...H G Brown deceased. Mr. Hughes is competent and worthy. You will remember that I wrote you about the vacancy and you were pleased to say that if I suggested a suitable name, the appt would be made. The appt of the above name will be most gratifying to me." The endorsement indicates that Hughes received the appointment desired

Together 3 items

$300-400

□ 108 BATES, KATHARINE LEE, *American Composer*. Autograph Transcription signed, 2 pages small 4to, n.p., being Miss Bates's transcription of the 4 verses of "America the Beautiful" ("O beautiful for spacious skies...," "O beautiful for pilgrim feet...," "O beautiful for heroes proved...," and "O beautiful for patriot dream..."); waterstained (with some of the stains affecting the signature); along with a photograph of Miss Bates, matted under blue velvet and framed

$1,000-1,500

☐ 109 DAVIS, JEFFERSON, *Confederate President.* Autograph Letter signed ("Jeffn. Davis"), 1 page 4to, Washington, D.C., 26 May 1854, to Caleb S. Hallowell in Alexandria, Va.; matted and framed with a photograph of Davis

A FAMILY CRISIS. Mrs. Davis's younger brother, Beckett Kempe Howell, came North with the family when Jefferson Davis was elected to the Senate. Young Beckett was a student of Hallowell, a Quaker schoolmaster in Alexandria, and here Davis writes with some irritation of the boy's condition on returning home: "Beckett returned here sick and soon after his arrival the measles was developed. This has detained him until the present date. I regret that he should have been exposed to this infectious disease, or if that was unavoidable, that I had not been informed of it, as serious inconvenience has resulted to my family from the want of information of Beckett's condition."

$400-600

☐ 110 GARFIELD, JAMES A., *Twentieth President.* Autograph Letter signed ("J A Garfield") as Presidential candidate, 1¼ pages 8vo, Mentor, Ohio, 23 August 1880, to John Dalzell of Caldwell, Ohio; replying to a recent letter from Dalzell, the Republican Presidential nominee remarks: "…I have written to Gen Nash advising him to give you appointments. Of course I do not feel like interfering [in] the conduct of the campaign but I want to see every force we have fully employed."

$300-400

☐ 111 GRANT, ULYSSES, *Eighteenth President.* Autograph Letter signed ("U.S. Grant Brig.Gen."), 1 page small 4to, Head Quarters, Dist. of Cairo, Fort Henry, Tenn., 7 February 1862, to Capt. Henry Walke, commander of the gunboat flotilla; a few scattered ink smears; matted and framed with a photograph of Grant in Civil Army uniform

FORTS HENRY AND DONELSON. The capture of these two forts on the Cumberland River in northern Tennessee was the first step in Grant's campaign in the West. It was essential that the Union destroy the Memphis, Clarksville & Louisville Railroad bridge eleven miles upriver from Fort Henry, and Grant's urgent message to Walke reads: "The party that went up the river last night for the purpose of destroying the R.R. bridge had to return without accomplishing their object in consequence of finding the bridge guarded. I would request that you go up with your boat to-day and take some twenty men that I will furnish to do the job." Walke's men found the job easier than anticipated, for when they arrived at the bridge, the rebels had already withdrawn, leaving the span undefended

Simon, *Grant*, vol. IV, 168-169

$750-1,000

☐ 112 GRANT, ULYSSES. Autograph Letter signed ("U.S. Grant"), 2 pages 8vo, New York, 4 June 1884, to S.C. Wright, secretary of the 28th Massachusetts Regiment Association; the two pages mounted one above each other to form a rectangle, matted and framed. Declining an invitation to join veterans of the regiment at a reunion later that month, Grant explains: "... I am still on crutches from injuries received from a fall in December last, and must expect to be for some time to come..."

$250-300

Mine eyes have seen the glory of the coming
of the Lord.
He is trampling out the vintage where the
grapes of wrath are stored,
He hath loosed the fateful lightning of His
terrible swift sword,
His day is marching on.

In the beauty of the lilies Christ was born
across the sea,
With a glory in his bosom that transfigures
you and me;
As he died to make men holy, let us die
to make men free,
While God is marching on.
Julia Ward Howe.
Boston Nov 8th 1868.

113

□ 113 HOWE, JULIA WARD, *American Poet*. Autograph Transcription signed, 1 page 4to, Boston, 8 November 1868, being Mrs. Howe's transcription of the first and last verses of "The Battle Hymn of the Republic" (i.e., "Mine eyes have seen the glory of the coming of the Lord..." and "In the beauty of the lilies Christ was born across the sea..."); browned, with wear at center horizontal fold; with an engraved portrait of Mrs. Howe, matted with marron velvet and framed

$1,500-2,000

☐ 114 JEFFERSON, THOMAS, *Third President.* Autograph Letter signed ("Th: Jefferson"), 1 page small 4to, Poplar Forest, 28 May 1815, to Col. Watts; browned, matted and framed along with a color reproduction of Peale's portrait of Jefferson and a photograph of the octagonal house designed by Jefferson for Poplar Forest

A STATESMAN'S BUSINESS AFFAIRS. Jefferson writes Watts of his efforts to exchange Treasury bills for bank bills: "... having learnt that the merchants in Lynchburg who deal to the Northward would willingly take treasury notes which served for remittances to other states in exchange for bank notes which would not be received there. I sent yesterday to Mr. Robertson to request him to procure me such an exchange. He answered by my messenger that I might count on the exchange & send on the Treasury bills. This I have done... I will be with you after an early breakfast tomorrow morning..."

$2,000-3,000

☐ 115 KENNEDY, JOHN F., *Thirty-fifth President.* Profiles in Courage. *New York, [1957]*

12mo. Plates; browned. Printed paper wrappers; a little used. Red buckram slipcase with black calf label

First paperback edition. PRESENTATION COPY, inscribed and signed by Kennedy on the title-page: "To a future Senator from Colorado Geoffrey Kneedler with best wishes John Kennedy." A nice association item from a crucial time in Kennedy's political career

Provenance: sold at Parke-Bernet, October 17, 1961, lot 160; the collection of S. G. Lorris, sold at Parke-Bernet, October 27, 1964, lot 175

$500-750

☐ 116 LINCOLN, ABRAHAM, *Sixteenth President.* Letter signed, 1 page ("A. Lincoln"), 1 page 4to, Washington, 2 April 1861, to Mrs. Mary Hancock Colyer at 105 Bleecker St., New York City; scattered soil; matted and framed along with an engraved portrait of Lincoln

LINCOLN RECEIVES A FAMILY SOUVENIR. Mrs. Colyer, a niece of John Hancock, had sent Lincoln a "share ticket" issued in Massachusetts in 1765, signed by her uncle and endorsed on the verso by the President's ancestor and namesake. Here he sends Mrs. Colyer his "... cordial thanks for the interesting relic you were so kind as to send me, as well as for the flattering sentiment with which it was accompanied."

Basler, vol. IV, p. 319

$1,500-2,000

118

□ 117 MONROE, JAMES, *Fourth President*. Autograph Letter signed ("Jas. Monroe") as American minister to France, 1 page small 4to, Paris, 19 September 1794, to [John Jay in London]; with Jay's endorsement on integral blank, lightly browned.

MONROE BEGINS HIS MISSION. Monroe had been named American envoy to France to succeed Gouverneur Morris, the aristocratic New Yorker who had alienated the French republican government. Here Monroe writes to Jay, who had been sent to England to negotiate an agreement that would settle American differences with Britain: "...I arrived here about the 4. of August. We sailed from Baltimore so that we can give you no intelligence of Mrs Jay & family since you saw them. Mrs. M. & child are well & thankful for yr. attention. Mr. Morris is still here and probably will be for some weeks to come..."

$300-400

□ 118 REVERE, PAUL, *American Patriot and Artisan*. Autograph Document signed twice, small oblong, Boston, 19 August 1793, being a receipt in Revere's hand reflecting the payment of David Greenough for "two Cast Iron backs... Window Weight... [and] One Iron back..."; signed by Revere at the foot of the receipt, with an integral signature in the document's heading "Bot of Paul Revere"; browned at edges; matted and framed along with an engraved portrait of Revere

$2,000-3,000

□ 119 [ROOSEVELT, FRANKLIN D., *Thirty-Second President*]. LINDLEY, ERNEST K. Franklin D. Roosevelt: A Career in Progressive Democracy. Indianapolis, [1931]

8vo. Front endpapers and rear fly-leaves browned from inserted newspaper clippings including portion of leaf with inscription, portion of 1 leaf (pp. 255-56) neatly clipped out and present in photo-facsimile. Original blue cloth; slightly rubbed, spine faded

First edition. ASSOCIATION COPY, inscribed and signed by Roosevelt on front free endpaper: "For my ancient Preceptor & friend George Marvin from Franklin D. Roosevelt." Marvin was a master at Groton during Roosevelt's last two years of attendance there and was later editor of the influential journal *World's Work*. He remained a lifelong friend of the thirty-second president

$200-300

□ 120 SMITH, SAMUEL F. Autograph Transcription signed, 1 page 4to oblong, n.p., 3 June 1887, being 4 verses of Smith's "America"; the verses written in two columns on the leaf; along with a photograph of Smith, matted and framed

$750-1,000

□ 121 WASHINGTON, GEORGE, *First President*. Autograph Survey signed ("G Washington"), 1 page 4to, [19 March 1751], being a survey of 300 acres near the head of Long Marsh River surveyed for by Washington for Patrick Rice; with Washington's hand drawn plat or scale drawing of the land at the top of the leaf and Washington's 12-line description of the plot beneath the drawing; 2 small ink blots in margins; 6 small taped repairs to splitting folds, scattered light soil and spotting; matted and framed with an engraved portrait of Washington ¶

WASHINGTON AS A SURVEYOR. Here Washington lays out Rice's 300 acres "... Beginning at three red Oaks in Limestone Ground comes to his late Survey [another survey made by Washington for Rice in 1750 of 400 adjoining acres] and extended thence So 22° W... to a low stand red Oak thence So 68° E... to a hicry and white Oak Sapling near a large white Oak in stoney Ground thence No 22° E... to two hicry and a red Oak in his line finally with his Line No 68° W... to the Beg long. Three hundred Acres" The land laid out in this survey was granted to George Rice on 7 March 1763 (Abbot and Twohig, *Washington*, vol. I, p. 26 and 27)

See illustration on next page

$6,000-8,000

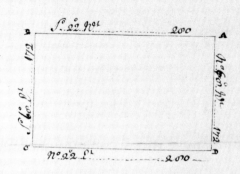

Pursuant to a Warrant from the Proprietors Office to me directed
I have Surveyd for Patrick Rice a certain tract of waste and un
granted Land joining the place whereon he lives and bounded as
followeth (Viz)

Beginning at three red Oaks in James Stone
Ground corner to his late Survey and extended thence S° 22° W°
Two hund° and Eighty poles to a locust and a red Oak thence S° 68° E°
One hund° and Seventy two poles to a hiccory and a white Oak Saplin
near a large white Oak in stoney Ground thence N° 22° E° Two hund°
and Eighty poles to two hiccorys and a red Oak in his line finally
with his line N° 68° W° One hund° and Seventy two poles to the
beginning Three hundred Acres

Thos. Balch   Jr.
Geo. Rice — Jld.
Benj. Harden — N°   G Washington

for if the latter is much cheaper, and the former difficult to be obtained, buildings will be so discouraged & the Sales so much impeded thereby, is to render the exclusion of Shingles unadvisable.

I am. Dear Sir Your affect.ᵗ & obt Servant

G: Washington

David Stuart Esq.ʳ

122

☐ 122 WASHINGTON, GEORGE, *as President.* Autograph Letter signed ("Go: Washington"), 1 page 4to, Philadelphia, 23 November 1791, to David Stuart; slightly browned, with some scattered spotting; matted and framed with an engraved portrait of Washington

THE PRESIDENT AND THE NEW FEDERAL CITY. In July 1790, Congress authorized Washington to name three commissioners to supervise the creation of the Federal District on the Potomac where the United States would erect its permanent capital city. Washington named his friend Stuart to the Commission, and in the spring of 1791, a survey of the district began under the direct of Pierre Charles L'Enfant, the brilliant French engineer. As work progressed, the District Commissioners found it increasingly difficult to work with the temperamental L'Enfant, and by the end of October, Stuart wrote Washington of their problems.

This is the second of two letters in which Washington attempted to smoothe matters between L'Enfant and the Commissioners, and he here writes Stuart with the utmost tact on a practical point: "After closing my letter to you of the 20th. I recollected that I had omitted to take notice of your observation respecting Wood covers to Brick or Stone buildings in the Federal City. It is much to be wished that this evil could be avoided without involving a greater, for it is difficult to decide between things to be wished — and things that are attainable. It has a claim however to consideration, & may be decided upon before the next general Sale. — In the meanwhile, it might be well to enquire, how far the measure would meet general approbation, — what probably, would be the difficulties in covering with slate, Tyle, or any thing else which would be proof against fire. — and what the difference in expence between these & Shingles: for if the latter is *much* cheaper, and the former difficult to be obtained, buildings will be so discouraged, & the Sales so much impeded thereby, as to render the exclusion of Shingles unadvisable." Washington's efforts to make peace between the commissioners and their chief engineer were fruitless. L'Enfant was discharged in February 1792, leaving others to execute his plan for the city that would bear Washington's name

Fitzpatrick, *Washington,* vol. XXXI, p. 427

$3,500-5,000

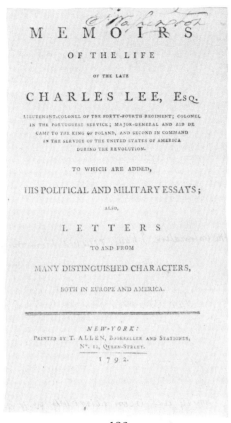

123

☐ 123 [WASHINGTON, GEORGE, *First President*]. [LANGWORTHY, EDWARD]. Memoirs of the Life of the Late Charles Lee, Esq. *New York: T. Allen, 1792*

12mo. Occasional minor foxing. Contemporary sheep, spine gilt with red morocco label; rubbed, front hinge cracked. Maroon morocco box gilt

First American edition, thick paper issue. ASSOCIATION COPY, from George Washington's library with his signature ("Go: Washington") on title-page.

The *DAB* refers to Lee as a "soldier or fortune [and] one of the most extraordinary and contradictory characters in American history." In volume II of *The Diaries of George Washington, 1748-1799* (Boston, 1925), the editor, John C. Fitzpatrick, writes that Lee was "an eccentric blusterer, of greater reputation than ability... Misbehavior on the field of Monmouth and subsequent actions caused his dismissal from the army. He wrote a criticism of Washington's management of the army which William Goddard published" (p. 175, note). Despite the antipathy of the two men, Washington owned at least one other copy of this work, sold in the Bushrod Washington auction of "George Washington Letters and Relics" (Henkels, 16 December 1891, lot 821). The Washington-Lee correspondence is included in the *Memoirs*

Evans 24456; Howes L83; Sabin 38903

Provenance: sold at Parke-Bernet, June 4, 1969, lot 166A

$6,000-8,000

Quincy April 27. 1817

Dear Sir

Mr Theodore Lyman jun.ʳ a Gentleman of a studious, inquisitive and irreproachable Character, is ardently desirous of seeing Gentlemen of Letters in England. The few, that I had the pleasure to know, excepting one or two, have departed to a World where I hope there are neither Politicks or Wars.

By the information I have received from my Son and grandson of your remembrance of me, I am encouraged to give Mr Lyman this simple introduction to you. His Father and his other Connections are wealthy and very respectable. Quite friendly enough to Great Britain.

What would I give? What would I not give? to spend a Month in London. But I must soon commence an Eternity, in other Worlds as I hope and believe.

Our Vanity has been tolerably well gratified by the last War, We are now in profound tranquility. More united and Unanimous than ever. How long this calm will last; how soon the Winds may rise, I know not.

I think however, upon the whole We have been very clever young Fellows to preserve a ~~few~~ Peace of thirty Years, when all your Europe was inflamed, and all of you constantly Studying to Spread your fires into our very combustible Wilderness.

I am Sir, with very pleasing Recollections, your Friend

Richard Sharp Esq, M.P.   John Adams

SIGNERS OF THE DECLARATION OF INDEPENDENCE

A fine set of autographs of all fifty-six of the men who signed the Declaration of Independence, along with an Autograph Letter signed by Ann Bourne Gwinnett, the wife of Button Gwinnett of Georgia. The Signers themselves are represented by: twenty-eight Autograph Letters signed, eight Autograph Documents signed, two Autograph Documents, fourteen Documents signed, one Autograph Endorsement signed, and three cropped Signatures. Of these, fifteen date from the Revolutionary era, with eight of these written in the year 1776

☐ 124 ADAMS, JOHN (*Massachusetts*). Autograph Letter signed, 1 page 4to, Quincy, 27 April 1817, to Richard Sharp in London; with soil on integral address leaf (Sharp's address in a hand other than Adam's)

ADAMS AND ENGLAND. Adams sends Sharp a letter of introduction for "Mr Theodore Lyman junr [1792-1849], a Gentleman of a studious, inquisitive and irreproachable Character." Adams apologizes for troubling Sharp and explains that Lyman "is ardently desirous of seeing Gentlemen of Letters in England. The few, that I had the pleasure to know, excepting one or two have departed to a World where I hope there are neither Politicks or Wars. By the information I have received from my Son and grandson [John Quincy and Charles Francis Adams] of your remembrance of me, I am encouraged to give Mr Lyman this simple introduction to you. His Father and his other Connections are wealthy and very respectable. Quite friendly enough to Great Britain."

Adams and Sharp had not seen each other since the 1780s, when Adams was American minister to London and Sharp was a young radical Whig. Thinking back to those days, Adams allows himself a moment of sentiment: "What would I give? What would I not give? to spend a Month in London. But I must soon commence an Eternity, in other Worlds as I hope and believe." As for Anglo-American relations today: "Our Vanity has been tolerably well gratified by the last war. We are now in profound tranquility. More united and unanimous than ever. How long this calm will last; how soon the Winds may rise, I know not. I think however, upon the whole We have been very clever Young Fellows to preserve a Peace of thirty Years, when all your Europe was in flames, and all of you constantly Studying to spread your fires into our very combustible Wilderness. I am Sir, with very pleasing Recollections, your Friend"

See illustration on previous page

$3,500-5,000

☐ 125 ADAMS, SAMUEL (*Massachusetts*). Autograph Letter signed ("S Adams"), 1 page small 4to, Philadelphia, 12 July 1775, to [James Warren]; lightly browned, with ink spots and seal stain, endorsed on verso; hinged to a larger leaf

ADAMS INTRODUCES ANOTHER "POOR" MAN. From the Continental Congress, Adams writes on behalf of a New York patriot: "Give me leave to recommend to your friendly Notice and to desire you would introduce into the Circle of our Friends Mr. Hugh Hughes of New York, a worthy sensible Man, whose Virtue has rendered him obnoxious to all the Tories of that City – He is perhaps as poor as I am, but he 'goes about doing good' ..." Adams closes with a gossip-hungry postscript: "pray write me particularly *of Men* as well as Events"

Smith, *Letters of Delegates*, vol. I, p. 623

$1,500-2,000

☐ 126 BARTLETT, JOSIAH (*New Hampshire*). Printed document accomplished and signed ("Josiah Bartlett Justo pacis"), 1 page small folio, Kingstown, N.H., 8 November 1774, being a deed from Edward Scribner of Kingstown to Reuben Lowell of Brunswick for 25 acres of land, accomplished and signed by Bartlett as justice of the peace; browned, endorsed on verso, taped repairs on verso to separating folds with some tape stains on recto and 2 small holes at intersections of the separating folds

$250-300

My dear Sir   Philad July 12 1775

Give me leave to recommend to your friendly Notice and to desire you would introduce into the circle of our Friend Mr Hugh Hughes of New York, a worthy sensible Man, whose Virtue has rendered him obnoxious to all the Tories of that City — I know I cannot say more to you in favor of any Man — He is perhaps as poor as I am, but he "goes about doing good" — I am sincerely your affectionate

S Adams

pray write me particulars of Men as well as Events

125

☐ 127 BRAXTON, CARTER *(Virginia)*. Autograph Letter signed, 1 page 4to, n.p., 9 July 1790, to Mr. A. Donald; slightly browned, scattered ink blots, address panel and endorsement on verso; inlaid in a larger leaf

A PLANTER'S CONCERNS. Braxton writes his business associate anxiously: "My want of Corn to support my Negroes is become very serious & I know not where to get it unless from you. If the exchange should be 33 ⅓ in next Month when you pay H. Heth, there will be some Money due to me for the last Tob[acc]o shipt you... since when I have only had 20 barrs. Corn & 2 barrs. flour – I must therefore trespass once more on your goodness for a supply of ten barrells Corn & I do promise you when a settlemt. of our Accts. to repay any balance that may be in your favour..."

$350-500

☐ 128 CARROLL, CHARLES, OF CARROLLTON *(Maryland)*. Autograph Letter signed, 1 page 4to, n.p., 16 February 1825, to a member of the Maryland legislature; lightly browned, heavier browning and soil at folds on verso, three tape remnants on verso's right margin

PUBLIC EDUCATION IN MARYLAND. Carroll writes his correspondent on several matters before the legislature of personal interest to him and his family as well as one concerning the public at large: "...A great part of the citizens of Baltimore are soliciting the Legislature to pass an act to establish free schools the persons advocating the act are generally needy: its passage is opposed by the corporation & the most intelligent & respectable Inhabitants, and several went off this morning to counteract this mischievous system..."

$250-300

☐ 129 CHASE, SAMUEL *(Maryland)*. Autograph Letter signed, 1 page 8vo, n.p., 25 March 1804, to Robert Goodloe Harper; with integral address panel bearing seal stain and 3 tape remnants, endorsed by Harper; writing a letter to be delivered by the black servant Isaac, Chase explains: "We did intend to purchase Isaac I was originally to have had him, but by accident ...Yates got him. He prefers living with you, and I wish you may purchase him – I did intend to go as far as 350 Dolls."

$350-500

☐ 130 CLARK, ABRAHAM *(New Jersey)*. Autograph Endorsement signed ("Abra: Clark, Shr."), 3 lines on the verso of the last page of a copy of a writ of inquiry, 2¼ pages small folio, [ca. June 1766]; browned, silked, with stains from taped repairs to folds, small marginal paper losses

$300-400

☐ 131 CLYMER, GEORGE *(Pennsylvania)*. Autograph Letter signed ("Geo Clymer"), 5 pages small 4to, Philadelphia, 30 May 1791, to Gen. Edward Hand; browned, some spotting, endorsed on verso of outer folded leaf, taped repairs to the central folds of the 2 folded leaves forming this letter's pages; hinged on another leaf

A SIGNER AND THE "WHISKY TAX." Clymer writes as supervisor for the Pennsylvania revenue district under the new "Whisky Tax," Hamilton's excise tax on liquor distilled in the United States. Hand was to be inspector of collection of the tax in Pennsylvania's "Survey # 3." Here Clymer attends to administrative details of their new offices: "...The visitation of the distilleries you will see is kept up in the secretary's expectation [i.e., Hamilton's lengthy circular letter on implementation of the new law, 26 May 1791, Syrett, Hamilton, vol. VIII, p. 365-387], 'tho in his late absence, in a conversation with the auditor Mr. Wolcoot ...I believe I satisfied him of the impracticality of realising it under the provision of the act. The idea of auxiliary Offices I am sorry to have like thoughts of. – I am glad you have so nearly gone through your round of information for within a fortnight we ought to take our final measures – previous to which a full consideration should be had of the numbers and arrangement of the collectorships in the survey – the secretary has said that one for a county will suffice, but he can mean this only as a limitation on one side against the excess, leaving the other open – if two counties could be thrown together in one range, and the service be as well performed, it would be abundantly more eligible..."

Clymer continues with "a note of the several applications made to me by persons within your survey..." for appointments in the countries under Hand's jurisdiction and remarks: "I know but some of these gentlemen and shall only remark with respect to one of them Dr H. [Dr J. Houston of Lancaster] that were he as active as he is good tempered no one could be better qualified – the Dr. has written me two letters but I never had the heart to tell him what I had often heard that his disposition was indolent. – Perhaps it is not so, but I refer him as well as every other to your better knowledge and judgment... your will recollect the Secretary asks a security from each of two thousand dollars..."

$500-600

☐ 132 ELLERY, WILLIAM *(Rhode Island)*. Autograph Letter signed, 1 page 8vo, Newport, 27 June 1775, to Nicholas Cooke in Providence, the letter also singed by James Clarke; browned, soil and seal tear on integral address leaf

RHODE ISLAND MOVES TO INDEPENDENCE. When the provincial legislature met in Providence a few weeks after the Battles of Lexington and Concord, Governor Joseph Wanton tried to block its efforts to aid the revolutionary war effort. Eventually the legislature simply ignored Wanton and suspended him from office until the fall of 1775, when Deputy-Governor Cooke was installed as Wanton's successor. Ellery and Clarke write from Newport, where they attempt to recover statistics from the records of the royal naval office: "Many necessary Avocations which have taken Place... have prevented us hitherto from doing any thing more than taking a View of the Naval Office Books; and from that View the taking an Accurate Account of the Produce and Manufacturers exported from the Colony and of the Imports not only by Water; but in fresh Provisions by Land from Connecticut and the Massachusetts will be a Work of Time – of the fresh Provisions brought into the Colony by Land an account can only be gained by an Enquiry of Butchers, Hog-killers &c. A Quire of Paper We imagine will not be more than sufficient to contain the almost endless Variety of Articles exported and imported, in Order to form a Summary, for One year only. The Exports and Imports from year to year for some years past have been so nearly alike, that an Account for One year will answer the Purpose. – Perhaps it may not be improper to lay this Matter before the Assembly. If it should be thought proper that We should proceed we will readily undertake the Business and hope We shall be able to exhibit an Account to August Session..."

$200-300

☐ 133 FLOYD, WILLIAM *(New York)*. Document signed, 1 page small 4to oblong, New York, 14 May 1784, being a pay order to Gerard Bancker, signed by Floyd and Isaac Roosevelt; browned, 2 small holes (not affecting text), receipt and endorsements on verso; authorizing Bancker to pay John Grenell "...for his Services in the Employ of the Commissioners for Procuring moneys on Loan & Clothing for the Use of this State..."

$250-300

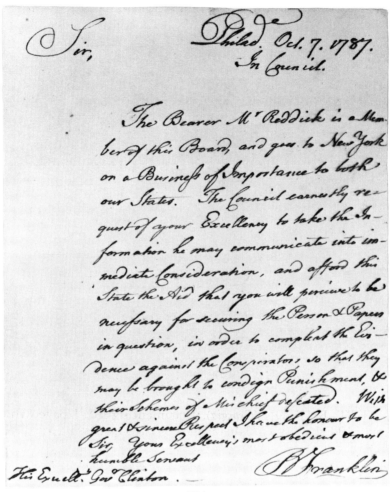

134

☐ 134 FRANKLIN, BENJAMIN *(Pennsylvania)*. Autograph Letter signed ("B Franklin"), 1 page 4to, Philadelphia, 7 October 1787, to Gov. George Clinton of New York; browned, skillful repair to seal tear on integral leaf, neat taped repairs to splitting fold joining the two leaves;

EXECUTIVE BUSINESS. Writing as President of the Pennsylvania Executive Council, Franklin furnishes a letter of introduction to Clinton for "...Mr. Reddick... a Member of this Board, [who]... goes to New York on a Business of Importance to both our States. The council earnestly request of your Excellency to take the Information he may communicate into immediate Consideration, and afford this State the Aid that you will perceive to be necessary for securing the Person & Papers in question, in order to compleat the Evidence against the Conspirators, so that they may be brought to condign Punishment, & their Schemes of Mischief defeated..."

$4,000-6,000

☐ 135 GERRY, ELBRIDGE *(Massachusetts)*. Printed Document signed as Governor of Massachusetts ("E Gerry"), accomplished in another hand, 1 page folio oblong, Boston, 24 April 1811, being Samuel Eastman's appointment as a captain in the state militia; paper seal intact, browned at folds, with several small holes in the weakened folds

$200-300

137

GWINNETT, BUTTON (*Georgia*). Document signed, 1 page 8vo oblong, Savannah, 19 February 1773, being a receipt for moneys received from Levi Sheftall, with 2 lines of text and figures in the lower lefthand corner in Gwinnett's hand; browned, some light staining and spotting, a few small paper losses (primarily at worn folds); endorsed on verso; silked and inlaid in a larger leaf

THE RAREST OF THE SIGNERS. Here Gwinnett, whose autograph is the most prized among the fifty-six Signers, signs a receipt reading: "Received Savannah 19th Feby. 1773 from Levi Sheftall four pounds two Shillings for his part of a debt due me by Mordecai & Levi Sheftall and in full of all Demands." After signing the receipt, Gwinnett himself has furnished this summary of his accounts with the Sheftalls in the lower lefthand corner of the leaf: "Deducted from Execution £ 2. 19" to which he adds "His Levi Sheftal's Acct– 1.3," giving the balance "£ 4:2 0"

The Sheftall brothers, members of one of Georgia's first Jewish families, were generally Gwinnett's creditors rather than his debtors, and it was to them that he deeded St. Catharine's Island in 1777 in an attempt to settle his long overdue accounts. This document is listed as # 34 in Dr Joseph Fields, "The Known Signatures of Button Gwinnett" (*New Colophon*, vol. III [1950]: 132-145)

Provenance: from the set formed by Alice Bemis Taylor and donated to Colorado College; sold to an anonymous collector in 1950; purchased by Paul Francis Webster at the Charles Hamilton Galleries, 18 October 1979

$100,000-150,000

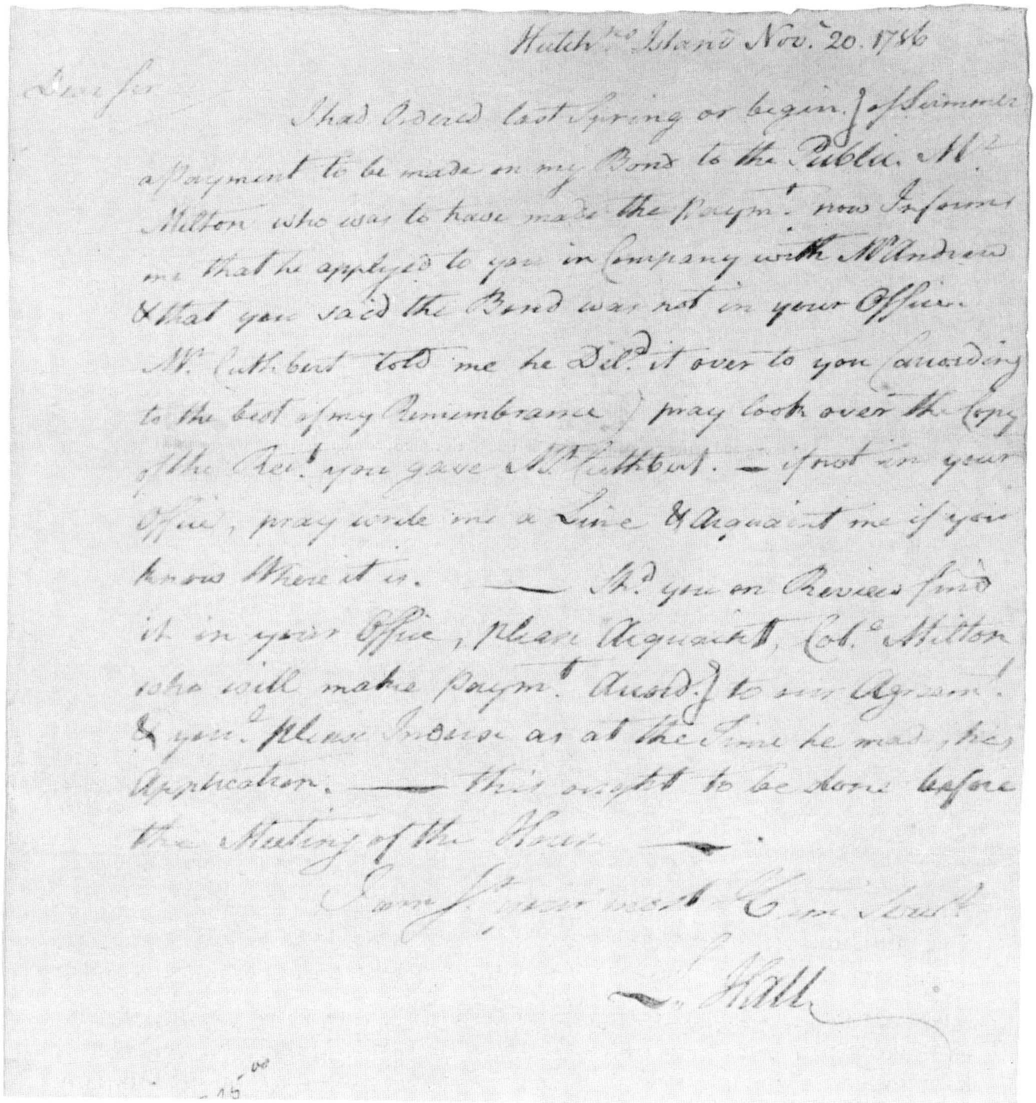

Hutch[inso]n Island Nov. 20. 1786

Dear Sir

I had Ordered last Spring or begin[in]g of Summer a payment to be made on my Bond to the Public. Mr. Milton who was to have made the paym[en]t now Informs me that he applyed to you in Company with Mr. Andrew & that you said the Bond was not in your Office. Mr. Cuthbert told me he Del[ivere]d it over to you (according to the best of my Remembrance) pray look over the Copy of the Rec[eip]t you gave Mr. Cuthbert. — if not in your Office, pray write me a Line & Acquaint me if you know Where it is. — Sh[oul]d you on Revisees find it in your Office, please Acquaint Col. Milton who will make paym[en]t (Agreeable) to our Agreem[en]t & you[r]? please Indorse as at the Time he made the Application. — this ought to be done before the Meeting of the House —

I am Sir your most Ob[edient] Serv[an]t

L Hall

138

☐ 137 GWINNETT, ANN BOURNE, *Wife of Button Gwinnett.* Autograph Letter signed ("A Gwinnett"), 1 page small 4to, Wolverhampton, 9 May 1765, to Richard Higgins at Pump Court Temple in London; lightly browned, substantial paper losses at margins (affecting the 2-line postscript), tape stains; address panel on verso bearing the red wax impression of GWINNETT'S SEAL

A SIGNER'S WIFE. During her husband's absence on a voyage, Mrs Gwinnett writes her attorney on a legal matter: "Mr Gwinnett being saild occasions me to send you the enclosed [not present]; imagining it concerns the suit, I beg leave to request your Correspondence about it you cannot blame me for my anxiety in an affair of such consequence; not doubting your compliance with an anwer..." The surviving portions of the postscript carry this poignant sentiment: "my sorrow for the loss of Mr G[win]nett is only to b[e] felt, [remainder missing]

$750-1,000

IN CONGRESS.

The DELEGATES of the United Colonies of *New-Hampshire, Massachusetts-Bay, Rhode-Island, Connecticut, New-York, New-Jersey, Pennsylvania,* the Counties of *Newcastle, Kent,* and *Suffex* on *Delaware, Maryland, Virginia, North-Carolina,* and *South-Carolina,* to *Levi Wells, Esq*

WE reposing especial trust and confidence in your patriotism, valour, conduct and fidelity, DO by these presents constitute and appoint you to be *Major to the twenty second Regiment of Foot, Commanded by Colonel Samuel Wyllys*

in the army of the United Colonies, raised for the defence of American Liberty, and for repelling every hostile invasion thereof. You are therefore carefully and diligently to discharge the duty of *Major* by doing and performing all manner of things thereunto belonging. And we do strictly charge and require all officers and soldiers under your command, to be obedient to your orders, as *Major* And you are to observe and follow such orders and directions from time to time as you shall receive from this or a future Congress of the United Colonies, or Committee of Congress, for that purpose appointed, or Commander in Chief for the time being of the army of the United Colonies, or any other your superior officer, according to the rules and discipline of war, in pursuance of the trust reposed in you. This commission to continue in force until revoked by this or a future Congress.

Attest *Cha Thomson secy*
January the first 1776

By Order of the Congress,
John Hancock President

139

☐ 138 HALL, LYMAN (*Georgia*). Autograph Letter signed ("L. Hall"), 1 page 4to, Hutchinstons Island, 20 November 1786, to Mr. Jones, the Georgia State Treasurer in Augusta; browned, soil and seal tear on integral address leaf

A FORMER GOVERNOR FIGHTS BUREAUCRACY. Hall writes wearily of his attempt to make a payment "... on my Bond to the Public. Mr. Milton who was to have made the paymt. now Informs me that he applyed to you in Company with Mr Andrew & that you said the Bond was not in your Office. Mr Cuthbert told he he Deld. it over to you (according to the best of my Remembrance) pray look over the Copy of the Rect. you gave Mr Cuthbert. – if not in your Office, pray write me a Line & Acquaint me if you know Where it is. – Shd. you on Review find it in your Office, please Acquaint Coll. Milton, who will make paymt. Accordg. to our Agreemt. & youl. please Indorse as at the Time he made his Application..."

$500-750

☐ 139 HANCOCK, JOHN (*Massachusetts*). Printed Document signed as President of the Continental Congress, accomplished in another hand, 1 page small folio oblong, [Philadelphia], 1 January 1776, being Levi Wells's commission as major in the 22nd Regiment of Foot commanded by Col. Samuel Wyllys, countersigned by Charles Thomson as Secretary of Congress; browned, scattered foxing; the verso partially backed by an oblong piece of paper to reinforce separating folds, with paper losses at margins and at intersections of folds (affecting a few characters of printed text)

$750-1,000

□ 140 HARRISON, BENJAMIN (*Virginia*). Autograph Letter signed ("Benjn Harrison"), 1¼ pages folio, Williamsburg, 31 October 1777, to Robert Morris in the Continental Congress at York, Pa.; with seal remnant on integral address leaf; browned, taped repairs to splitting horizontal fold, fold joining letter and address leaf completely separated (with tape remnants from an earlier repair)

PREMATURE CONGRATULATIONS. Just returned to Virginia from service in Congress, Harrison writes Morris on reports of the American victory at Saratoga: "I most sincerely congratulate you on the very good News we have from the North, but more so on the acct. we have Recd. of Washingtons being once more in possession of Philadelphia this last," rumor, Harrison admits "is not so well authenticated as I could wish yet I believe it, as I have seen one line from under the Postmasters hand at your York which informs us of the fact, we suppose Mr Howe did not chuse to stand a second attack and has retreated to his Ships below Chester, but this is all guess work, no Man here being favord with a Line from Congress, or any one in it, a matter of no small Mortification to me, if it should be true that Philada is again ours pray make my very particular compliments to Mrs Morris on the joyful occasion, I [pray?] her worthy Breast will be again at rest and that she may no more meet with the alarms and distresses she has encountered lately..."

The rumor of Philadelphia's evacuation by the British was, of course, unfounded. Mrs Morris would not be able to return to her home until the following summer. Harrison's letter continues with news of the legislative session in Virginia: "I can venture to assure you that what members I have seen seem very well disposed to support with Vigour the American Cause, but the other States must do the same, they will never be the Pack Horses of America your Resolutions in the [Articles of] Confederation that all States shall be equal as to their Votes gives great, and I think just uneasiness and you may assure yourself will never go down if there should be one more obnoxious article, which I am very apt to think will be the Case, thr'o the fears and apprehensions of some, and the jealousies and designs of others, my earnest wish is that an accomodation betwixt the States may take place, and no endeavours of mine shall be wanting to bring it about on just and equitable terms, but I neither can nor will sacrafice my Country–"

Harrison closes on a practical note, turning to matters of mutual mercantile interest to himself and Morris: "I shall shortly have much leasure on my Hands, can you in your goodness think of no way to employ me. I love an active Life and will not spare myself to serve my Family or Friends, very great advantages may be made by a trip to S. Carolina if a Number of Waggons could be got to send there, I would even take that trip and wait... if you can think of any thing that will be of Service to you and myself fix your own terms and I will conform to them, and I make no doubt of giving you satisfaction..."

$2,000-2,500

□ 141 HART, JOHN (*New Jersey*). Document signed, 2 pages small folio, [Hopewell, N.J.], 6 July 1768, being an inventory of the estate of Thomas Anderson of Hopewell township, signed by Hart and Daniel Drake; browned, stained, silked

$250-300

☐ 142 HEWES, JOSEPH (*North Carolina*). Cropped Signature, on a small oblong apparently cropped from a manuscript account, bearing Hewes's signature below the line "Errors Excepted/ £ 185.19.2"; browned, wear at margins

$175-225

☐ 143 HEYWARD, THOMAS JR. (*South Carolina*). Printed Document signed ("Thos Heyward Junr"), accomplished in another hand, 1 page folio oblong, Charleston, 13 June 1788, being a legal document; endorsements on verso

$100-125

☐ 144 HOOPER, WILLIAM (*North Carolina*). Document signed, 1 page 4to, Salisbury, N.C., 6 March 1769, being a grand jury indictment of Lewis Hutton for breaking and entering; browned, badly waterstained, marginal paper losses, splitting at 2 horizontal folds

$350-500

☐ 145 HOPKINS, STEPHEN (*Rhode Island*). Printed Document accomplished and signed twice, 1 page folio, Providence, 29 and 30 October 1733, being a mortgage deed from Elisha Hopkins; signed once by Stephen Hopkins as the justice witnessing Elisha Hopkins's personal appearance and a second time as town clerk recording the deed; wax seal intact, browned at folds, wear at margins

$300-400

☐ 146 HOPKINSON, FRANCIS (*New Jersey*). Autograph Letter signed ("Fras. Hopkinson"), 1 page 4to, Philadelphia, 11 December 1778, to the American Commissioners at Paris; browned, minor foxing; left margin attached to an oblong strip, apparently once part of a mount; writing as the Treasurer of Loans, Hopkins sends the commissioners a list of loan office bills

$300-400

☐ 147 HUNTINGTON, SAMUEL *(Connecticut)*. Autograph Letter signed ("Saml Huntington"), 2½ pages small 4to, Norwich, Conn., 12 April 1776, to Jabez Huntington in Norwich, Conn.; with integral address leaf and with Jabez Huntington's draft reply to this letter, 7 May 1776, on the verso of the address leaf; browned, seal tear (affecting a few characters of Jabez's draft reply), spotted, with Huntington's franking signature ("Sm Huntington Free") on the address leaf

A SIGNER WRITES HIS KINSMAN. Huntington reports: "...the Congress have been exceeding busy commonly set from ten in the morning until between 4 & 5 in the afternoon without any refreshment... hope we shall be able to obtain for N London harbour a number of the heavy cannon brot. in there by Commodore [Esek] Hopkins we are Endeavouring to obtain some assistance from Congress to fortify that Harbour as an asylum for the Continental fleet..." In his draft reply, Jabez Huntington reports another matter that may need Congressional attention: "Doc Turner [says] that a Number of the Sick men belonging to the Continental Fleet are now in Hospitall at N London visited p[er] him & he apprehends a Hospital will be Fixed there for the purpose & would be willing to be appd. to some Department for that Hospital from his Experience in the Army & known Skill in Surgery..."

Smith, *Letters of Delegates*, vol. III, p. 515

See illustration on next page

$750-1,000

147

□ 148 JEFFERSON, THOMAS (*Virginia*). Autograph Letter signed ("Th.: Jefferson"), 1 page 4to, Paris, 2 March 1786, to Giovanni Fabbroni; slight browning, small seal tear on integral blank

AN UNPUBLISHED LETTER. Jefferson explains his delay in writing Fabbroni: "I have for sometime deferred the honor addressing you, in expectation that our friend mr [Philip] Mazzei on his return from Holland, would go on immediately to Florence..." A change in Mazzei's plans forces Jefferson to write Fabbroni directly now "to return you my thanks for the pamphlets you were so kind as to inclose to me, and from the perusal of which I received very great satisfaction, that relative to the value of lands being particularly applicable to our plan of taxation in America, I consider as very precious, & filled with useful ideas. I hope you have before this received the book I took the liberty of sending you thro' mr Favi; a medley little worth your notice but of some avail to me as it has furnishd me an occasion of testifying the sentiments of esteem & respect with which I have the honour to be Sir Your most obedient & most humble servant"

$2,500-3,000

☐ 149 LEE, FRANCIS LIGHTFOOT *(Virginia)*. Autograph Letter signed, 1¼ pages small folio, Menokin, 2 July 1773, to his brother William Lee in London; with restoration to seal tears on integral address and 2 small tears to letter, the letter and its leaf browned and silked

FAMILY BUSINESS MATTERS. Francis Lee writes his brother on the problems of finding a ship to send tobacco to London: "...you have lost near 300 h[ogs]h[ea]ds for want of ship room; as there will be a great deal of tobo. left in the Country & the present crop is very forward..., I think you shou'd have a ship as early as possible in the fall in the country. I am afraid Hipkins will be tardy in making his remittances, I have press'd him often & warmly... You may depend I will be as bad as a third day ague & fever to him untill he complys..." He continues with tales of the irresponsibility of local boatmen: "we are endeavouring to form some regulations for these Gentry agst. the next meeting of the Assembly, the trade suffers so much by their negligence & villainy that every body is convinced of the necessity of taking them under consideration..." He closes on a more personal note: "Mrs. Lee intended to have sent her Sister some hams by Dobbie, but the Captn. assured me it was impossible to keep them in a summer passage... I am afraid I am so far behind with you, that my tobo. will not pay the ball[ance]: & answer the Goods to be sent for... but you may depend I will remit you in bills next summer, before the tradesmen will be clamorous for their money... please to give our hearty love to our dear Sister & Brother Lawyer [Arthur Lee, then embarked on a second career in the law after training as a physician]..."

See illustration on next page

$2,000-2,500

☐ 150 LEE, RICHARD HENRY *(Virginia)*. Autograph Letter signed, 2½ pages 4to, Chantilly, Va., 20 January 1782, to an unidentified correspondent in South Carolina; lightly browned, expert restorations to seal tear and other paper losses on the second leaf (affecting one character of signature), fold joining the 2 leaves reinforced, glue stains on verso

THE SOUTH AFTER YORKTOWN. Lee responds with delight to a letter opening a correspondence with the gentleman to the South, remarking: "... I perceive that our great obligations to you are not likely to cease so long as the enemy continue their hostility against us. The change in our southern affairs has been wonderful indeed since the beginning of the year 1781. Now, the enemy seem by their 'very respectful' conduct, to have left you little more to do until we can be assisted by a marine force; for I suppose that, whatever may be the case with Savannah, Charles Town cannot be recovered by us, unaided by a fleet. It would appear, if it is not decreed above that Great Britain shall no longer be counted among the nations of the earth, that the fall of Cornwallis, your successes in the south, and the progress of France in the west Indies must produce a speedy peace..."

He assures him that: "Our Assembly have done every thing in their power to give content to the army, and they have not omitted a plan for recruiting our line of the Continental forces – how far the latter will succeed, time may shew – its success will depend very much upon the wisdom and vigor of the executive, with the activity of the recruiting officers..."

$750-1,000

My dear Brother   Menokin July 3d 1773

By a Glasgow ship I am certain that Mr. M. Smith intended to ship 80 hhd tobo in Rayson to answer the bills he had drawn
on you, but as he could not take them in, we have tryd since he would fail
to charter you have lost near 300 £ for want of ship room; As there will
be a great deal of tobo left in the country & the present crop is very forward
& promising, I think you should have a ship as early as possible in
the fall in the country. I am afraid Hipkins will be tardy in making
his remittances, I have pressd him often & warmly, he has promised me
to remit you by the first opportunity £90 which he had in hand, and
£100 for which he expected an order from Col. Taylo, besides 100 hhd of
tobo. which he is hawking about for sale the produce of which he
assures me will be remitted to you. You may depend twill be as
bad as a third day ague & fever to him untill he comply. John Gordon
says he does not know what he owes you, as you have not sent him
sales nor Acct. curr.; every body is so ready at evading demands, that
it is impossible to collect debts without having an exact state of their
Accts. which you shoud allways send me, at least of those whom
you intend I shoud push for payment. I wrote you by the Justitia Capt.
Gray, but he is not yet saild, & I doubt will not before Rayson,
when she does, John Corrie is to draw for his ball. on Campbell.
Capt. Rayson just left me, his last craft is now taking her load from the
lower parts of this River, he is allready, & will sail as soon as this craft
gets round, he has been much troubled with the crafts on er; indeed they are
grown so bad, that it requires a person much better acquainted with
this business & much cleverer than Rayson to manage them, we are
endeavouring to form some regulations for these Gentry agst the next
meeting of the Assembly; the trade suffers so much by their negligence
& villainy that every body is convinced of the necessity of taking them
under consideration. my 22 hhd are on board, you will insure so as to
recover £6 in case of loss. I hope if we shd have a war it will not raise
insurance much, as our opponents are not very powerfull at sea.
Mrs. Lee intended to have sent her sister some hams by Dobie, but the last
assured me it was impossible to keep them in a summer passage, so we
have deferd it till the fall, & shall be glad to have a conveyance in a
ship of your own. I am afraid I am so far behind with you, that my
tobo. will not pay the ball. & answer the good to be sent for by Rayson
but you may depend I will remit you in bills next summer, before the

149

☐ 151 LEWIS, FRANCIS *(New York)*. Autograph Letter signed ("Frans. Lewis"), 1 page 4to, New York, 28 February 1761, to Thomas Riche; lightly browned, with heavier discoloration at left margin, a few small holes and slight splitting at one fold, endorsed on verso; requesting a Mediterranean passport for a ship in which he is concerned: "...The Vessell will sail in about Ten days therefore beg Your answer by the first & please to let me know the Cost thereof." As for military affairs: "Yesterday arived here his Majesties Ship Grayhound... with dispatches for the General in Compy with this Ship saild Four Frigates & Three Bombs. for the Missicippie, & an Expedition for Martinico is also talked of..."

$250-300

☐ 152 LIVINGSTON, PHILIP *(New York)*. Autograph Document with 3 integral signatures ("Phil. Livingston"), 8vo oblong, New York, 17 April 1761, being a receipt for £400 paid by Philip Livingston to John Livingston and signed by John at the foot of the document; browned, endorsed on verso; Philip pays the sum "...for the use of Jillis Fonda... in part payment of the bond from him and George Klock to Phil. Livingston..."

$350-500

Lynch

153

☐ 153 LYNCH, THOMAS JR. (South *Carolina*). Cropped signature ("Lynch"), mounted on a larger leaf along with an Autograph Letter signed by Lyman C. Draper, Hillsdale, Calif., 13 January 1890, certifying "...that this Lynch signature was discovered & obtained from a descendant of a sister of the Signer... since the printing of my Essay on the Autograph Collections of the Signers of the Declaration of Independence & of the Constitution – it was taken from the fly-leaf of a volume of Swift's Works, published in London, in 1766, preserved in the family of that sister since the Signer's death; & having thoroughly compared this Signature with other genuine Lynch signatures, I am prepared to assert and guarantee its genuineness."

This signature is one of those falling into Dr. Joseph Fields's category # 1, inscribed ca. 1766, and characteristic of the signature as inscribed in Lynch's set of Swift ("Thomas Lynch, Jr. and his Autographs"; see also, Fields's "A Signer and His Signatures or the Library of Thomas Lynch, Jr.," p. 229-236, for an exhaustive history of the Lynch signatures removed from the Swift edition)

$3,500-5,000

☐ 154 McKEAN, THOMAS *(Delaware)*. Printed Document signed ("Thos M:Kean"), 1 page folio oblong on vellum, Philadelphia, 15 April 1805, being a the grant for "Rosehill" in Northampton County, Pa., to Philip Nicklin and Robert Griffith, signed by McKean as governor of Pennsylvania; paper seals intact, endorsed on verso, some paper losses at lower margin

$100-150

☐ 155 MIDDLETON, ARTHUR (*South Carolina*). Autograph Draft Document, 11 lines, 1 page small 4to, [Philadelphia, 28 January-19 February 1782], being Middleton's draft of a resolution on Vermont, inscribed on the integral blank of Thomas Bee's draft of a letter from the South Carolina delegates to Governor Rutledge, 1½ pages, Philadelphia, 27 January 1782; browned, wear at margins and folds, discoloration at the top margin of the first page of Bee's letter

MIDDLETON AND VERMONT. On 28 January Middleton was named to Congress's "grand committee" considering procedures for admitting Vermont to the Union. The committee made its report on 19 February, and the document offered here is a resolution drafted by Middleton during the committee's sittings: "The latter part of the Report [i.e., the report referred to this committee in late January] seems intended to allure the dissenting States [i.e., states like New York and New Hampshire that disputed Vermont's claims] to a compliance, by giving the Face of an Act of power to what would in reality be a humiliating Condescention; We have been & continue oppos'd to the admission of a 14th. State for reasons which appear to us cogent; among others because it will throw a Ballance of Power where it is not wanted & because it will be a precedent for future Divisions of the larger States – but above all because Congress have no power to grant such admission, & the only ground hitherto pleaded for the Measure has been that of policy & not of Right."

Middleton inscribed this fascinating explication of his views of the powers of Congress and sectional interests on the leaf used by his colleague Thomas Bee to draft a joint letter from the South Carolina delegates to Governor Rutledge the day before Middleton was named to the committee on Vermont

$2,500-3,500

☐ 156 MORRIS, LEWIS (*New York*). Autograph Document signed, 1 page small oblong, New York, 28 April 1796, being a promissory note from Morris to W. S. Smith for $120; slight browning, 2 small holes, endorsed on verso, inlaid in a larger leaf

$250-300

☐ 157 MORRIS, ROBERT (*Pennsylvania*). Printed Document signed ("Robt. Morris") as President of the North American Land Company, accomplished in another hand, 1 page 4to oblong, Philadelphia, 18 April 1795, being a certificate for ten shares in the company made out to William Temple Franklin, the grandson of Benjamin Franklin and one of the European agents for Morris's land speculations; browned at edges (probably reflecting an earlier framing), slight ink smears

$250-300

☐ 158 MORTON, JOHN (*Pennsylvania*). Autograph Document signed, 1 page folio, n.p., 11 November 1761, being evidence taken by Morton as sheriff in the dispute between Henry Platt v. Margaret Sweeney; lightly browned, taped repairs to splitting horizontal folds, endorsed on verso, inlaid in a larger leaf; containing the testimony of Henry Platt, a merchant who charged that Sweeney had stolen 6½ yards of calico and a "ramnant of Check linnen" from his shop, and from Alice McGloughlin, Sweeney's landlay

$250-300

□ 159 NELSON, THOMAS (*Virginia*). Document signed ("Thos Nelson jr"), 2 pages small folio, War office, Richmond, 24 July 1782 (?); being a draft of an order concerning state regiments, signed by Nelson as "Approv'd in Council"; browned, with many emendations, paper losses at one splitting fold, other small holes and tears, docketed: "Respecting the soldiers belonging to the state regiments joining Colo. Dabney's at different places of rendezvous"; directing "All soldiers, belonging to the regiments formerly known by the names of the first and second state, the state garrison, and state artillery... to join the new regiment composed of those several corps... Such deserters from any of those corps, as shall surrender themselves to some state officer at a place of rendezvous on or before the fifteenth day of September next shall be pardoned; those that neglect this humane offer, may be assured that no pains shall be spared to apprehend them and bring them to the severest punishment..." and setting the points of rendezvous at Williamsburg, Petersburg, Fredericksburg, Prince Edward court house, Staunton, and Winchester, with the Goochland Courthouse as the point of "general rendezvous"

$800-1,200

□ 160 PACA, WILLIAM (*Maryland*). Autograph Draft Letter signed ("Wm. Paca"), 1 page 4to, Annapolis, 27 December 1783, being a circular letter to members of the Maryland Council, drafted by Paca as governor; browned, spotted, and foxed, endorsed on verso; writing the Councillors: "... I have thought proper to notify to you that public Business requires the Council to be convened on Monday the fifth Day of January at which Time your attendance is requested."

$350-500

□ 161 PAINE, ROBERT TREAT (*Massachusetts*). Autograph Letter signed ("R T Paine"), 1½ pages small 4to, n.p., 30 May 1789, to Judge Sumner at Roxbury; with integral address leaf, browned, some ink blots, endorsed on address leaf

A MERCIFUL ATTORNEY GENERAL. Paine writes Sumner concerning two men whom Paine had prosecuted before the Supreme Judicial Court at Worcester the preceding term. The men, John Dunsmore Sr. and Jr., had been convicted of "riot" and were jailed when they could not pay their fines and court costs. Now Paine reports: "... I am informed by Capt. Josselyn the Representative of New Braintree (the Town where the Dunsmores live) that money may be collected to pay the Sons fine & half the Cost, but that the Sheriff says that he cannot release the son from Prison unless the whole Cost be paid. From what I heard at the Tryal as well as what Capt. Josselyn now tells me I believe the Son to deserve a good Character saving this particular, (to the Commission of which he was compelled by his Father), there is no great prospect that the father will be able to pay the Costs & I submit to your Honor's Consideration whether it is not best to permit the Sheriff to take the Sons fine & half the Costs & release him that he may return to his Family & go to work..."

$750-1,000

time We, who are of the Committee of Correspondence for the Delaware Government, are Gentlemen

your most obedient humble Servants.

[signatures]

163

☐ 162 PENN, JOHN (*North Carolina*). Autograph Document signed ("J Penn"), 1 page folio, n.p., 4 April 1784, being Penn's acknowledgment of the delivery of a receipt for a share in the Bank of North America, inscribed on the verso of George Clymer's and John Nixon's Printed Letter signed ("Geo Clymer" and "John Nixon"), Philadelphia, 31 May 1781, to Thomas Burke; slightly browned, spotting in margins, stain at top margin (affecting first paragraph of printed letter), wear at vertical and horizontal folds with expert restoration of 3 holes in these folds (affecting a few words of the printed text and one character of the date line in Penn's manuscript receipt on the verso)

THREE SIGNERS AND THE BANK OF NORTH AMERICA. The printed and manuscript texts and signatures on this remarkable document highlight the connections of three Signers of the Declaration of Independence – Penn, Clymer, and Robert Morris – with America's first attempt at a national bank. In 1781 the Bank of North America was one of the cornerstones of the policies of Morris, the newly appointed Superintendent of Finance. In their circular letter, Clymer and Nixon inform prominent men in the various states of the bank's creation, enclosing a copy of a plan for the institution (not present) devised by "... Mr Morris, superintendant of finance elect and approved of by Congress, on the twenty seventh instant..." Clymer and Nixon were authorized to choose agents "to solicit and receive..." subscriptions to the shares in the Bank, and this copy was sent to Burke, then the governor of North Carolina, to act as agent in Hillsborough, "your well known attachment to the cause of your country leaving us no room to doubt of your zeal, and readiness, to fulfill the end of your appointment..." Clymer and Nixon enclosed fifteen receipts for shares in the Bank, directing Burke to send any funds subscribed to Philadelphia as soon as possible

Burke died in December 1783, and Penn apparently assumed his duties as the Bank's agent in North Carolina. (Burke had earlier served as Morris's receiver of taxes for the state.) On the verso of the printed circular that had been Burke's authorization for the agency, Penn records: "Recd. of Mr James Hogg one Receipt sent by Messrs. Clymer and Nixon to Mr Thos Burke as mentioned in the within circular letter to be sent to Mr Morris"

$2,000-3,000

☐ 163 READ GEORGE *(Delaware)*. Autograph Letter signed ("Geo: Read"), 2¼ pages small 4to, New Castle, Dela., 26 May 1774, being a circular letter from the Delaware Committee of Correspondence to the Virginia Committee of Correspondence, in Read's hand and also signed by Thomas McKean and John McKinly; browned, taped repairs to splitting folds, inlaid in another leaf

THE BOSTON PORT BILL. Read and his colleagues appeal for coordinated resistance to the closing of the port of Boston: "...We consider each Colony on this Continent as parts of the same Body, and an attack on one to affect all. The people of Boston are singled out on this occasion by the British Ministry for Apparent Reasons, and if they can succeed so far as to procure a submission, the like or some such Experiment will be made on each Colony in turn; if this shou'd happen, there would be an End to American Freedom for a Century at least..." The Delaware committee calls for a suspension of all trade with Britain as a measure that "wou'd not only alarm in turn, but procure Applications for our relief from those, who, in all likelyhood wou'd be more favourably heard than the Americans [i.e., British merchants]... The Conduct of the British Parliament on this occasion, so derogatory of the Character which that senate once had, needs no Comment, a Shadow of Justice, a Cloak of Power used for America's Scourge indicates the necessity of a Congress of Deputies from the several Colonies to determine and agree upon further Measures for redress at present or future Grievances... As the Inhabitants of this Government entertain a high opinion of the Zeal and firmness of those of your Colony in the Common Cause of America, We are persuaded that their resolutions at this important Crisis will have great Weight here, and we shall be glad to have your Sentiments thereon..."

Both Read and McKean would serve in the First Continental Congress when it met that fall to consider united action against British imperial policies and would sign the Declaration of Independence in the summer of 1776

$1,000-1,250

☐ 164 RODNEY, CAESAR *(Delaware)*. Autograph Letter signed, 3 pages small 4to, Philadelphia, 21 August 1776, to his brother Thomas Rodney in Kent County, Dela.; lightly browned, mounting remnants on verso and 4 small tears resulting from dismounting (not affecting text)

A POLITICAL SETBACK. Rodney writes on learning the results of elections in Kent for delegates to Delaware's first constitutional convention: "... Read an account of your defeat in the Election and in which I was not disappointed – being Convinced you Continued to be Sanguine in your Expectations without taking the Necessary Steps to Carry a point of that Sort – added to all the rest of your bad policy you Suffered Caldwell's Company to March away just before the Election... Parke tells me the Conduct of ye Light Infantry heretofore, had Drawn down the resentment of the people which put it in the power of that party Who were opposed to you, to make this Use of it..." He offers this comfort to his brother about the loss of the election: "The present Convention is solely for the purpose of frameing Government and will not be allowed to go out of that line... The people may therefore perhaps think better of ye Matter next time they Choose..."

Smith, *Letters of Delegates*, vol. V, p. 43

$1,000-1,500

☐ 165 ROSS, GEORGE *(Pennsylvania)*. Autograph Document signed ("G: Ross atty. p Deft by Specl. Warrt:"), 1 page folio, Lancaster County, November 1763, being a confession of judgment for Ross's client, attorney David Henderson, in an action brought by Alexander Adair; lightly browned, with heavier browning at folds, verso with endorsement and taped repair to separating center fold

$150-200

☐ 166 RUSH, BENJAMIN *(Pennsylvania)*. Autograph Letter signed ("Benjn: Rush"), 1¼ pages small 4to, [Philadelphia], 9 October 1804, to an unidentified correspondent; slightly browned, soil and spotting on second page; writing to introduce a Mr Bean, who "... comes strongly recommended to me from New Hanshire as a person qualified to teach a female School. I have mentioned his Name and objects in the northern liberties where I was encouraged to believe he would be successful. I beg leave to refer him to you for further advice and assistance in his Undertaking – If he be like many of the gentlemen educated in New England, he will cooperate with you in your ministerial labors in the above District in sowing the Seeds of just principles in the minds of the lambs of your flock."

$400/600

☐ 167 RUTLEDGE, EDWARD *(South Carolina)*. Autograph Letter signed ("Ed: Rutledge"), 1 page 4to, Charleston, 5 August 1791, to Samuel Saxon, sheriff at Ninety-Six District; browned, with integral address leaf, browned, silked, with neat taped repairs to folds on address leaf; Rutledge writes: "I find that the Lands at Ninety-Six, which were fornerly Mr Salvadore's, & which were sold at the Suit of Mr Bourdeaux, were knocked off to me – You will be pleased to make the Conveyances to Mr Peter Freneau."; the page also bearing Robert Goodloe Harper's Autograph Endorsement signed, 24 January 1792, acknowledging a statement at the foot of the page signed by a Charleston justice of the peace that Harper had heard Rutledge acknowledge having written the letter of August 1791 that appears at the head of this leaf

$150-200

☐ 168 SHERMAN, ROGER *(Connecticut)*. Document signed, 1 page small 4to oblong, New Haven, 27 October 1777, directing the sheriff of Fairfield County to summon Ephraim Burton to appear before the county court at New Haven, signed by Sherman as an Assistant; browned, some spotting, mounted on a larger leaf

$150-200

☐ 169 SMITH, JAMES *(Pennsylvania)*. Autograph Document signed, 1 page folio, York County, October 1783, being the narrative and judgment in Smith's action against John Irwin; with 3 additional full integral signatures and 5 partial integral signatures ("James"); lightly browned, with heavier browning at folds, endorsed on verso, inlaid in a larger leaf

$250-300

☐ 170 STOCKTON, RICHARD *(New Jersey)*. Autograph Note signed ("Richd. Stockton"), 1 page 4to, Morven, 12 July 1773, to William Bradford, "Printer & Stationer," in Philadelphia; with integral address leaf; browned and discolored, seal tears on address leaf partially repaired; asking Bradford to send "... by the next Stage half dozen Skins of parchment..."

$500-750

☐ 171 STONE, THOMAS *(Maryland)*. Autograph Letter signed ("T: Stone"), 1¼ pages large 8vo oblong, n.p., 2 February 1774, to an unidentified merchant-correspondent; browned, restorations to marginal paper losses, inlaid in a larger leaf

AN APOLOGETIC DEBTOR. Stone writes sheepishly to his creditor: "I wish heartily my Ability was equal to my Inclination to pay the Balance due by me to your Company – when I promised you it was in Consequence of Engagements to Myself for double the Sum I need for you, in which I have been very unexpectedly disappointed – I have the greatest Reason to believe I shall receive Money very soon & when I do shall immediately call on you. More I can't do, tho I should be extremely sorry that you should want one Moment what is due from Me..."

$1,000-1,500

☐ 172 TAYLOR, GEORGE *(Pennsylvania)*. Cropped signature ("Geo: Taylor") on a small oblong; faint spotting

$350-500

☐ 173 THORNTON, MATTHEW *(New Hampshire)*. Autograph Manuscript, 2 pages small 4to, n.p., n.d. [1790s?], being a fragment of a theological treatise; browned and spotted, inlaid in a larger leaf; the passage in this fragment concerning free will and predestination begins: "He hath Shewed thee O Man, what is Good, & what Doeth the Lord Require of thee, but to do justly, Love Mercy, & Walk Humbly before God. – This, & many more Mistakes, arises from not Rightly Considering the Nature & perfections of the Creator, & the Nature, & powers, he has Delegated to Creatures, any proposition that is Contrary to any of the Known perfections of the Creator, is a Mistake Or Contrary to the Nature he has given his Creature. This Mode of Blaming others, with our faults Began Earely, Adam, Endeavered to Excuse himself, by laying the Blame on Eve, & Eve on the Serpent... The Advocates, for our having lost all power of doing Good, by Adam's first Transgration, Appear to Consider the Body as the Whole Man & it is true, that as far as Adam, & Eve's Bodies was Concerned, all their posterity Suffers the Consequencies of their Eating the forbiden fruit..."

$300-400

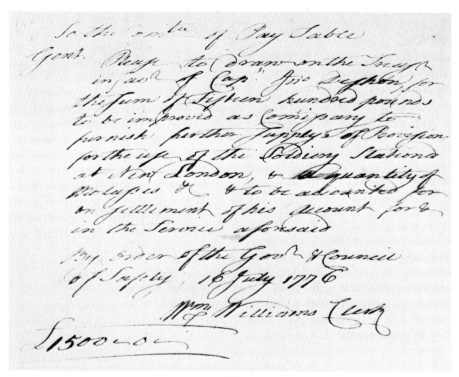

176

☐ 174 **WALTON, GEORGE** *(Georgia).* Autograph Letter signed, 1¼ pages folio, Savannah, 1 March 1776, to William Goddard, Inspector General of the "Constitutional Post-Office"; with integral address leaf, lightly browned, scattered foxing, with splitting or separation at most folds, paper loss in upper lefthand corner (affecting 3 characters of the salutation and one word of the second page of the letter), the tear extending to the address panel, extensive seal tears to address panel as well

GEORGIA MOVES TOWARD INDEPENDENCE. Walton reports proudly to Goddard, surveyor of the Continental postal service: "Since your departure from this place, we have purged our Council, and have now a full Board, composed of men, in my opinion, as warmly attached to the American Cause, as our Friends – of New-England: We set night and day, and have proceeded to make the best postures of Defence possible. Insomuch, that we have been able to effect an entire union among the people, and we now are in exceeding good spirits. We are preparing several... Vessels to annoy the Cherokee & her Retinue, and also erecting a small Battery in the field below the town, in order to play upon them at the same time. We have irrevocably determined that not a single Rice ship, of those now in our Port, shall be permitted to sail until the further sense of the Continental Congress shall be known..."

Walton assures Goddard that the patriot cause is better organized than it appeared when Goddard visited Savannah to set up the post office: "I am sorry that you left us quite so soon: you, perhaps, would have gone away with more genuine notions of southern Virtue than, I am afraid, our distractions, when you were here, impressed – Endeavour to remove them..."

$2,000-2,500

□ 175 WHIPPLE, WILLIAM *(New Hampshire).* Autograph Letter signed ("W Whipple"), 2½ pages folio, Philadelphia, 17 March 1776, to his brother-in-law, Dr Joshua Bracket of Portsmouth, N.H.; browned, stained, with crude repairs to marginal paper losses and splitting folds (affecting a few characters of text), address panel on verso

WHIPPLE LOOKS FORWARD TO INDEPENDENCE. Promising Bracket "some accot of affairs" outside New England, Whipple reports: "... Every war like Preparation is making at N. York, two Brigadier Generals viz Thompson, & Lord Sterling, are there 8,000 men are order'd there, & requisitions to Connecticut, New York, & New Jersey, to hold their Militias in readiness to go to the assistance of York, if needful... Commissioners are to set off for Canada in a few days they have with them two Roman Catholick Gentn: of Merriland [Charles Carroll of Carrolton and Father John Carroll] warm Friends to the American Cause, one of them an Ecclesiastick there is no doubt in my Opinion but that Province will be secured to the United Colonies. Baron De Woedlke who is taken into the Continental service is also going there... he is well acquainted with the French Language & I suppose has a long string of titles which will please them People..."

He continues with news brought by the latest packet arrived at New York: "... Our Friends in England recommend Firmness in the strongest terms. Its fully expected that the late acts of Parliament (Justifying the Pirates in seizing & destroying American Property & confiscating all American Property wherever to be found) will cause a final separation, in short administration themselves can think no other as is evident from their setting scriblers to work to shew that the Colonies are of but very little Consequence to Britain, it may be depended on that no assistance can be obtained from Russia, it is also an undoubted fact that 20,000 men is the utmost they will be able to get to America this summer... & this you may be assur'd of inter Nos that France stands ready to assist us whenever we ask her. − now Sir," he asks, "what have we to fear? Powder is almost daily arriving in small Quantities & there is the greatest prospect of an ample supply of all military stores shall we in these circumstances Bow the knee to B? God forbid..."

He closes with this account of Ethan Allen's fate after his capture at Montreal the preceding September: "these Gentn that came in the Packet left London ye 23 Dec: & Falmouth 7th Jany− they saw Col: Allen in Pendeniss Castle in Irons but before they left Falmouth he was sent on Board a man of war to do duty as a Common Sailor this ship is coming to America, − can there be an American so lost to Humanity as to wish a connection with [such a] set of Barbarians..."

Smith, *Letters of Delegates,* III, p. 395-396

$3,500-5,000

□ 176 WILLIAM, WILLIAM *(Connecticut).* Autograph Document signed ("Wm Williams Clerk"), 1 page small 4to, [Hartford]. 16 July 1776, being an order from the Governor and Council of Safety of Connecticut directing the committee "of Pay Table" to pay Capt. John Deshon £1,500 "... to be improved as Comissary to furnish further supplys of Provision for the use of the Soldiery Stationed at New London..."; browned and foxed, with Deshon's signed receipt on verso; inlaid in a larger leaf

$1,000-1,250

☐ 177 WILSON, JAMES *(Pennsylvania)*. Autograph Letter signed, 1 page small 4to, Philadelphia, 28 September 1782, to Jasper Yeates; small seal tear on integral address leaf, slightly browned, some spotting; hinged on another leaf; writing on court matters, Wilson promises: "… You may depend on my Punctuality on the first of November – I have not forgot how much you obliged me…"

$400-600

☐ 178 WITHERSPOON, JOHN *(New Jersey)*. Autograph Document signed ("J. W."), 1 page small oblong, n.p., 11 May 1776, being Witherspoon's account with Lewis Pintard, a New York merchant; removed from a larger leaf; with docket "Dr Witherspoon's Acct… Paid" on the verso of the integral blank; browned, small hole in blank; inlaid in a larger leaf; recording Witherspoon's debts to Pintard for "Sundry Books & Paper furnished" and with Witherspoon's direction "Pay the above to the same Gentleman"

$1,000-1,500

☐ 179 WOLCOTT, OLIVER *(Connecticut)*. Autograph Letter signed, 3 pages small 4to, Philadelphia, 16 November 1776, to Samuel Adams (of Litchfield?); browned, slight staining, endorsed on verso

WOLCOTT REPORTS TO AN ADAMS. The Adams to whom Wolcott writes here is probably the Litchfield lawyer who was the father of Congressman Andrew Adams. The Connecticut Congressman gives his friend an up-to-the-minute report on public affairs: "… An Expedition is supposed to be forming by the Enemy, Many Think agt. this City in Consequence of which Expectation, all the associators are ordered to it. I think it is more probably they will go farther South, I think, to the Carolinas or Georgia. Some Very Considerable Success has been had agt. the Cherokees, a Number of their Towns have been burnt, so that it is hopd. these Savages will be thoroughly quelld…"

He writes of the difficulties of establishing a new Continental Army: "it is an established Opinion here and amongst all the Officers of the Army, that the pay of it must be uniform, An Army it is said under different pay cannot subsist together – and that for any Colony to Vary in this Circumstance is totally to Subvert a continental Regulation, which if it could be done, it is in Vain to make any – for if the Views of a particular Colony were answered, and a new & general Regulation took place in Consequence of it, another Colony might Vary from that, and so render every Regulation ineffectual…" He closes with a description of his plight as the only delegate left to represent Connecticut. Despite his responsibilities, he promises: "I will Endeavour while here to be even with you in the Letter Writing Way but if at any Time I should fail I hope it will be no Discouragement to your perseverance only I Wish that it might be a little quickened – my best Regards to my Friends"

Smith, *Letters of Delegates*, vol. V, p. 507-508

$1,000-2,000

would instirely put a stop to all Business,
but for some Reason or I will not conjecture
what, he was Determined and has gone home,
I believe more Colonies will soon be in
N York Wants one more Member for a
Representation who is hourly expected, Delaware
and Maryland Members are settling their
Government, Georgia Representation expire
the 1 of this Month and their Members are
Waiting for New Powers. — I perceive by a
Philadelphia paper Published there is under the N Haven
Head, that the former Connecticut Members
are re elected with Mr Law. — whether they
are all to attend, or some of us to happily
Vacancies I have not heard, and indeed nothing
more about it, then what I saw in that Paper

I will endeavour while here to be
even with you in the Letter Writing Way
but if at any Time I should fail I hope it
will be no Discouragment to your perseverance
only I Wish that it might be a little
quickened — my best Regards to my friends
I am Sir
your most Obedient
humble Servant
Oliver Wolcott —

Saml Adams Esqr

179

☐ 180 WYTHE, GEORGE *(Virginia)*. Document signed ("G Wythe"), 3 pages
4to, Richmond, 24 November 1786, being Wythe's signed attestation that the
deposition that appears in the first 2½ pages of the document was duly
signed by Andrew Ronald; with paper seals intact, uniformly browned,
paper seals intact

$400-600

181

□ 181 CLASSICAL VENEERED MAHOGANY SECRETARY BOOKCASE, New York, circa 1815, in two parts: the upper having a straight pediment over two glazed, Gothic-mullioned cupboard doors opening to shelves; the lower section with a recessed bank of five short drawers and a hinged folding writing surface over one long and two short drawers, the whole on spiral-turned legs ending in carved paw feet. *Height 7 ft. 10 in. (2.34 m.); width 47 in. (1.2 m.); depth 24 in. (61 cm.)*

Provenance: PRESIDENT FRANKLIN DELANO ROOSEVELT, from his study at Hyde Park, formerly owned by the President's mother, Sara Delano Roosevelt; bequeathed to the President's son James and sold by him at Ames Art Galleries, Beverly Hills, CA, April 27, 1953, lot 75 (copy of the catalogue included)

$7,000-9,000

END OF SALE

SOTHEBY'S
FOUNDED 1744

Absentee Bid Form:

Sotheby's 1334 York Avenue,
New York, N.Y. 10021
Bid Department (212) 606-7414

Important: Please see
"Guide for Absentee Bidders"
on the reverse of this sheet.

Sale Title:	Date:	Sale Code:
Library of Paul Francis Webster	April 24, 1985	"WEBSTER" - 5313

I wish to place the following bids for this sale to be held on April 24, 1985. These bids are to be executed by Sotheby's up to but not exceeding the amount or amounts specified below. Each bid is PER LOT, as indicated, and all bids will be executed and are accepted subject to the "Conditions of Sale" and "Terms of Guarantee" printed in the catalogue of this sale. Please note that a premium of 10% will be added to the hammer price as part of the total purchase price.

Lot Number	Item	Top Limit of Bid not including 10% premium (Bid is per lot number as listed in the catalogue)
		$
		$
		$
		$
		$
		$
		$
		$
		$
		$
		$
		$

Arranging Payment

In order to avoid delays in receiving purchases, buyers unknown to us are advised to make payment arrangements or supply credit references in advance of the sale date. If such arrangements are not made, purchases cannot leave our premises until checks have been cleared.

Please Mail to:
Sotheby's Bid Department
1334 York Avenue, New York, N.Y. 10021

Name (please print or type)

Date

Address

City, State   Zip Code   Telephone
☐ Please check if this is a new address.

Bank reference or deposit (If bidder is unknown to Sotheby's)

Signed   Resale Number (If applicable)

9/84 BS

Guide for Absentee Bidders

Absentee Bids
If you are unable to attend an auction in person, and wish to place bids, you may give Sotheby's Bid Department instructions to bid on your behalf. Our representatives will then try to purchase the lot or lots of your choice for the lowest price possible, and never for more than the top amount you indicate. This service is free and confidential. Please note: Sotheby's offers this service as a convenience to clients who are unable to attend the sale, and although we will make every effort, Sotheby's will not be responsible for error or failure to execute bids.

Placing Absentee Bids
To place bids, please use the absentee bid form provided in this catalogue. Be sure to accurately record the lot numbers and descriptions and the top price you are willing to pay for each lot. "Buy" or unlimited bids will not be accepted. Always indicate a "top limit" – the amount to which you would bid if you were attending the auction yourself.

Alternative bids should be indicated by using the word "OR" between lot numbers. Then if your bid on an early lot is successful, we will not continue to bid on other lots for you. Or, if your early bids are unsuccessful, we will continue to execute bids for alternative lots until a bid is successful. Bids must always be placed in the same order as the lot numbers appear in the catalogue.

Each absentee bid form should contain bids for one sale only; the number and code name should appear in the top right hand corner of the form. Please place your bids as early as possible. In the event of identical bids, the earliest received will take precedence.

Telephone Bids
Bids may be placed by telephone, but are accepted only at Sotheby's discretion and at the caller's risk. Telephone bids should always be confirmed by letter or telegram.

Buyer's Premium
The "top limit" you indicate on your bid form is for the hammer price exclusively. Please keep in mind that a premium of 10% will be added to the hammer price of each lot you buy and is payable by you together with the applicable sales tax which is applied to the total cost of your purchase. (The total cost includes the buyer's premium).

Successful Bids
Successful bidders will be notified and invoiced within a few days of the sale. All bidders will receive a list of sale results if they purchased the sale catalogue or enclose a stamped self-addressed envelope with their absentee bid form.

For More Information
To place telephone bids, or for further information, please call Roberta Louckx at (212) 606-7414, or the regional office in your area.

Guide for Shipment of Purchases

Shipping/Forwarding Instructions
If your bid is successful, we can arrange to have your property shipped to you. As shipping costs can be expensive, we suggest that you request a quotation from our Art Transport Department at (212) 606-7511. If an estimate of shipping costs is not requested prior to shipment, we will act according to the instructions you provide. All shipments will be C.O.D.

The packing and shipping of items by Sotheby's employees is undertaken solely at our discretion. Furniture, larger items and high-valued property may require the services of professional packers.

Upon receipt of payment, Sotheby's will instruct packers and carriers. Your attention is drawn to the Conditions of Sale which require payment and clearance promptly after the sale. In default of these conditions, lots may be transferred to a public warehouse at the risk and expense of the purchaser. As stated in the Conditions of Sale, we are not responsible for the acts or omissions of carriers or packers, whether or not recommended by us. Packing and handling of purchased lots by us is at the entire risk of the purchaser.

Please allow 2-3 weeks for delivery.

Methods of Transport
Air Freight – Not to be confused with air mail, this method employs air freight carriers to ship property that has already been packed.

Registered Parcel Post – Parcels which do not exceed the size and weight limits set by the United States Postal Service may be sent by this method. In the case of international shipments, it is not always possible to insure parcels for their full value. Please consult the Art Transport Department for details.

Truck – This method is recommended for large shipments and the transport of any item of furniture. There are also "shuttle services" which can transport uncrated paintings and works of art to specific areas in the United States. The Art Transport Department can supply complete details.

Book Post – This is a less expensive, but slower, method of shipping books via the United Postal Service. Parcels shipped in this manner can be insured only for a maximum of $400.

For More Information
To receive an estimate of shipping costs, or for further information, please call Eileen Baral at (212) 606-7511, or the regional office in your area.

Photography:
Robert Lorenzson and Noel Allum
of Sotheby's Photography Studio
Tel.(212) 606-7210

Illustrations in this, or any, Sotheby's catalogue are available for purchase. For more information, please call Sotheby's Photography Studio at (212) 606-7210.

Color Separations
BCK Graphic Arts SA

Printer
Printed in Switzerland by BCK Graphic Arts SA
Geneva

SOTHEBY'S

FOUNDED 1744

Headquarters

1334 York Avenue, New York, N.Y.
10021. Telephone: (212) 606-7000,
Cables: Parkgal, New York. Telex: from
abroad New York 232643 (SPB UR),
from USA and Canada 125380
(SPB NYK)

Regional Offices and Associates

U.S.A.

Baltimore
Aurelia Bolton *(Associate)*
P.O. Box 250
Riderwood, Maryland 21139
Telephone: (301) 583-8864

Beverly Hills
Barbara Pallenberg
Christine Eisenberg *(Associate)*
308 North Rodeo Drive
Beverly Hills, California 90210
Telephone: (213) 274-0340
Telex: Los Angeles 677120 (Abinitio LSA)

Boston
Patricia Ward
101 Newbury Street
Boston, Massachusetts 02116
Telephone: (617) 247-2851

Chicago
Catharine C. Hamilton
840 N. Michigan Avenue
Chicago, Illinois 60611
Telephone: (312) 280-0185

Dallas
Mary Lide Kehoe *(Associate)*
5941 Woodland
Dallas, Texas 75225
Telephone: (214) 361-6662

Hawaii
Andrea Song Gelber *(Associate)*
P.O. Box 177
Honolulu, Hawaii 96810
Telephone: (808) 526-0170

Houston
Flo Crady
2501 River Oaks Boulevard
Houston, Texas 77019
Telephone: (713) 528-2863

Miami
Areta Adler Kaufman *(Associate)*
P.O. Box 144969
Coral Gables, Florida 33114-4969
Telephone: (305) 854-0313

Nashville
Mary Bit (Mrs. Alfred W.) Taylor *(Associate)*
P.O. Box 50419
Nashville, Tennessee 37205
Telephone: (615) 329-0446

Newport
Marion Oates Charles *(Associate)*
Betsy D. Ray *(Associate)*
288 Spring Street
Newport, Rhode Island 02840
Telephone: (401) 846-8668

New York City
C. Hugh Hildesley *(Associate)*
Lee Copley Thaw *(International Representative)*
Telephone: (212) 606-7110
Lynne Stair *(Associate)*
Telephone: (212) 606-7180

Palm Beach
Gigi Tylander
Hope P. Kent *(Associate)*
155 Worth Avenue
Palm Beach, Florida 33480
Telephone: (305) 833-2582
Miami (toll free number): (305) 947-2239

Philadelphia
Wendy T. Foulke
1811 Chestnut Street
Philadelphia, Pennsylvania 19103
Telephone: (215) 751-9540

San Francisco
Anne Horton
Lisa Hubbard
Mrs. John N. (Dodie) Rosekrans *(Associate)*
210 Post Street
San Francisco, California 94108
Telephone: (415) 986-4982

Washington, D.C.
Sara Dwyer
Marion Oates Charles *(Associate)*
Mrs. Joan F. Tobin
(International Representative)
2903 M Street NW,
Washington, D.C. 20007
Telephone: (202) 298-8400

CANADA

Geoffrey P. Joyner, President
Christina Orobetz
9 Hazelton Avenue
Toronto, Ontario M5R 2E1
Telephone: (416) 926-1774
Helene Desmarais *(Associate)*
759 Victoria Square, 7th Floor
Montreal, Quebec
Canada H2Y 2K4
Telephone: (514) 487-9194

MEXICO

Interart, S.A. de CV
Sandra Weisenthal
(International Associate)
Asociados Internacionales
Campos Eliseos 65
Mexico, D.F. 11580
Telephone: (905) 531-7800

Sotheby's International Realty

Bruce Wennerstrom
Chairman and President
James Phelps Retz
Executive Vice President
Executive Offices
1334 York Avenue
New York, New York 10021
Telephone: (212) 606-7660

Sotheby's Appraisal Company

(Insurance and Estate
Appraisals)
Michael Grogan, *Director*
1334 York Avenue
New York, New York 10021
Telephone: (212) 606-7440

Sotheby's Restoration

(Furniture)
John Stair, *Director*
440 East 91st Street
New York, New York 10128
Telephone: (212) 860-5446

Please refer to inside back cover for directory of Overseas Auction Rooms and Representatives

International auction locations and representatives

UNITED KINGDOM
London
34-35 New Bond Street,
London W1A 2AA and
Bloomfield Place
(off New Bond Street)
Telephone: 44 (1) 493-8080
Telex: 24454 SPBLON G

Chester
G. H. S. Bailey, A.R.I.C.S.
Booth Mansion,
28 Watergate Street,
Chester, Cheshire CH1 2NA
Telephone: 44 (244) 315531
Telex: 61577 SOBART G

Pulborough
W. L. Weller, F.R.I.C.S., F.S.V.A.
The Pulborough Salesrooms
Pulborough
West Sussex RH20 1AJ
Telephone: 44 (7982) 3831
Telex: 87210 GAVEL

Cambridgeshire
Mark Armstrong
56 High Street, Trumpington,
Cambridge CB2 2LS
Telephone: 44 (223) 67624

Cumbria and Northumberland
The Earl of Carlisle, M.C., F.R.I.C.S.
Market Place, Brampton,
Cumbria CA8 INW
Telephone: 44 (6977) 3666
or
Market Place, Haltwhistle,
Northumberland NE49 OBU
Telephone: 44 (498) 20363

Dorset
George Kidner
42 Holdenhurst Road,
Bournemouth, Dorset BH8 8AF
Telephone: 44 (202) 294425/6

Exeter
John Tremlett
Bickham House
Kenn
Exeter EX6 7XL
Telephone: 44 (392) 833416

Gloucestershire
John Harvey
18 Imperial Square, Cheltenham
Gloucestershire, GL50 1QZ
Telephone: 44 (242) 510500

Lancashire
Susan Yorke
Hall Foot, Worston
Clitheroe, Lancashire BB7 IQA
Telephone: 44 (200) 41520

Lincolnshire
Lady Victoria Leatham
The George Hotel Mews,
Station Road
Stamford, Lincolnshire PE9 2LB
Telephone: 44 (780) 51666

Somerset
Robert Dalgety
Magdalene House
Magdalene Street,
Taunton, Somerset TA1 1SB
Telephone: 44 (823) 88441

Suffolk
Lord Cranworth
Grundisburgh
Woodbridge Suffolk IP13 6TW
Telephone: 44 (47 335) 581

Wiltshire
Lord Seymour, A.R.I.C.S.
Maiden Bradley
Warminster BA12 7HW
Telephone: 44 (98 53) 525

Yorkshire
John Phillips
8-12 Montpellier Parade, Harrogate,
North Yorkshire HG1 2TJ
Telephone: 44 (423) 501466/7

Vanessa Towers
Green Hammerton,
Telephone: 44 (901) 30931

Charles Wyvill
Constable Burton Hall, Leyburn,
North Yorkshire DL8 5LJ
Telephone: 44 (677) 50361

Scotland
John Robertson
112 George Street
Edinburgh EH2 4LH
Telephone: 44 (31) 226 7201

Anthony Weld Forester
146 West Regent Street
Glasgow G2 2RQ
Telephone: 44 (41) 221 4817

Earl of Aboyne
Aboyne Castle, Aberdeenshire
Telephone: Banchory (033 02) 4007

Channel Islands
Enquiries to: Robin Townley
Sotheby's Valuations Department
Telephone: 44 (1) 493-8080

ARGENTINA
William R. Edbrooke
Kerteux Antiques
Libertad 846, Buenos Aires
Telephone: 54 (1) 393 0831
Telex: 9900 BTH SA AR
Attention: Bill Edbrooke

Mrs. Mallory Hathaway de Gravière
Avenida Quintana 475
Buenos Aires
Telephone: 54 (1) 44 64 18

AUSTRALIA
Melbourne
Ann Roberts
606 High Street
East Prahran
Melbourne, Victoria 3181
Telephone: 61 (3) 519152
Telex: MARQAA 33076

Sydney
Robert Bleakley
13 Gurner Street,
Paddington
Sydney, New South Wales 2021
Telephone: 61 (2) 332 3500
Telex: SPBSYD AA2563

AUSTRIA
Dr. Agnes Husslein
Palais Breuner,
Singerstrasse 16, 1010 Vienna
Telephone: 43 (222) 524772/3
Telex: 111868 SKA A

BELGIUM
Count Henry de Limburg Stirum
32 Rue de l'Abbaye,
Brussels 1050
Telephone: 32 (2) 343 50 07
Telex: 61339, SPBBXL B

BRAZIL
Rio de Janeiro
Walter Geyerhahn
Rua do Rosario 155
2° Andar
Rio de Janeiro 20041
Telephone: 55 (21) 252 1415 &
252 7973 & 252 7719

Sao Paulo
Cornelius O. K. Reichenheim
Alameda Ministro Rocha
Azevedo 391
Sao Paulo 01410
Telephone: 55 (11) 282 1599 &
282 0581

DENMARK
Baroness
Hanne Wedell-Wedellsborg
Bredgade 27
1260 Copenhagen K
Telephone: 45 (1) 13 55 56

FRANCE
Marc Blondeau
3 Rue de Miromesnil
75008 Paris
Telephone: 33 (1) 266 4060
Telex: SPBF A 640084F

GERMANY
Cologne
Ursula Niggemann,
St. Apern-Strasse 17-29,
(Kreishaus Galerie)
D-5000 Cologne 1
Telephone: 49 (221) 249330
Telex: 8882744 SOTK

Frankfurt
Johannes Ernst
Christiane Gräfin zu Eltz (Consultant)
Steinstrasse 7,
D-6000 Frankfurt/M.70
Telephone: 49 (69) 62 20 27
Telex: 413479 SOTHF-D

Hamburg
Peter Graf zu Eltz
Alsterkamp 43
2000 Hamburg 13
Telephone: 49 (40) 4 10 60 28

Munich
Dr. Ernst Behrens
Odeonsplatz 16, D-8000 Munich 22
Telephone: 49 (89) 22 23 75/6
Telex: 523443 ABNIT D

HOLLAND
Jan Pieter Glerum
John Van Schaik
102 Rokin, 1012 KZ Amsterdam
Telephone: 31 (20) 24 6215/6
Telex: 13267 MAKSO NL

HONG KONG
Mrs. Mamie Howe
P.O. Box 83,
705 Lane Crawford House,
64-70 Queen's Road Central
Hong Kong
Telephone: 852 (5) 248121
Telex: 75486 LANE HX

IRELAND
William Montgomery
The Estate Office, Greyabbey
Newtownards, Co. Down
Telephone: 353 (24 774) 392
and
123a Upper Abbey Street, Dublin 1
Telephone: 353 (1) 734811

Mary Boydell (Consultant)
Dublin
Telephone: 353 (1) 322021

Julia Keane (Consultant)
Cappoquin
Telephone: 353 (58) 54258

ISRAEL
Dov Hoz 19
Tel Aviv
Telephone: 972 (3) 226616
Telex: 361 595 DANET IL

ITALY
Florence
Count Alvise di Robilant
Palazzo Capponi
Via Gino Capponi 26,
50121 Florence
Telephone: 39 (55) 2479021
Telex: 572478 ABINIT I

Milan
Laura Grandi
Via Montenapoleone 3,
20121 Milan
Telephone: 39 (2) 783907
Telex: 322098 ABINIT I

Rome
Sofia Bosco
Palazzo Taverna,
Via di Monte Giordano 36,
00186 Rome
Telephone: 39 (6) 656 1670 &
654 7400
Telex: 623282 ABINIT I

Turin
Lauro Russo
Corso Galileo
Ferraris 18B
Turin
Telephone: 39 (11) 54498

JAPAN
Miss Kazuko Shiomi
Pisa Counter, Tokyo Prince Hotel
3-1-1 Shiba-koen,
Minatoku, Tokyo 105
Telephone: 81 (3) 437-1916
Telex: J23255 SEIBPISA
Attn: Miss Kazuko Shiomi

MONACO
Leon Leroy
B.P. 45, Le Sporting d'Hiver,
Place du Casino,
MC 98001, Monaco Cedex
Telephone: 33 (93) 30 88 80
Telex: 479471 SPBMON MC

NORWAY
Ingeborg Astrup
Bjornveien 42
0387 Oslo 3
Telephone: 47 (2) 1472 82

SOUTH AFRICA
Cape Town
Miss Susan Loppert
Guarantee House
37 Burg Street
Cape Town 8001
Telephone: 27 (21) 23 4728

Johannesburg
Stephan Welz
4th Floor, Total House,
Smit Street, Cnr. Rissik Street,
Braamfontein, Johannesburg
Telephone: 27 (11) 339-3726/7
Telex: 4-22261 SA

SPAIN
Edmund Peel
Enrique G. de Calderon
Plaza de la Independencia 8
28001-Madrid
Telephone: 34 (1) 232 6488/6572
Telex: 46787 SPBS E

SWEDEN AND FINLAND
Baron Nils von Essen
Arsenalsgatan 4,
111 47 Stockholm
Telephone: 46 (8) 101478/9
Telex: 17380 SPBCAN S

SWITZERLAND
Geneva
Nicholas C. Rayner
Bruno Muheim
24 Rue de la Cité,
CH-1204 Geneva
Telephone: 41 (22) 21 3377
Telex: 429098 SPB CH

Zurich
Dr. J. G. Wille
in partnership with
Alfred Schwarzenbach
20 Bleicherweg, CH-8022 Zurich
Telephone: 41 (1) 202 0011
Telex: 815 333 SOTH CH

TAIWAN R.O.C.
Rita Wong
147 Chien Kuo, North Road,
Section 2,
Taipei, Taiwan, R.O.C.
Telephone: 886 (2) 531-6226
Telex: 28514 INVEST EC

In illo tempore.
Cum natus
esset ihesus in
bethleem iude, in diebus &c